The AR-15 Assembly Guide and Service Manual

HOW TO BUILD AND SERVICE THE AR-15 RIFLE

Erik Lawrence

The AR-15 Assembly Guide and Service Manual

HOW TO BUILD AND SERVICE THE AR-15 RIFLE

by Erik Lawrence

published by Erik Lawrence
copyright © 2023 Erik Lawrence
copyright © 2015 Erik Lawrence
copyright © 2013 Erik Lawrence

Printed and bound in the United States of America

First printing 2013

Second printing 2014

ISBN-13: 978-1-941998-40-3

eBook ISBN - 978-1-941998-41-0

ATTENTION US MILITARY UNITS, US GOVERNMENT AGENCIES AND PROFESSIONAL ORGANIZATIONS
Quantity discounts are available on bulk purchases of this book. Special books or book excerpts can also be created to fit specific needs. For information, please contact Erik Lawrence via email at support@vig-sec.com.

WARNING
Firearms are potentially dangerous and must be handled responsibly by individuals. The technical information presented in this manual reflects the author's research, beliefs, and experiences. The information in this book is presented for academic study only. Neither the author nor the publisher assumes any responsibility for the use or misuse of information contained in this book.

SAFETY NOTICE
Before starting an inspection, ensure that the weapon is unloaded and cleared. Do not manipulate the trigger until the weapon has been cleared of all ammunition. Inspect the chamber to ensure that it is empty and no ammunition is present. Keep the weapon oriented in a safe direction when loading and handling.

AMMUNITION NOTICE
Firing the incorrect ammunition will damage the weapon and possibly injure the operator.

TRAINING NOTICE
Training should be received from knowledgeable and experienced instructors on this particular weapon system. Vigilant Security Services, LCC provides this training and continually perfects its instruction with up-to-date information from actual use.

vig-sec.com

TABLE OF CONTENTS

SECTION 1

Introduction

The objective of this manual is to allow the reader to be competently able to assemble an AR-15 rifle from parts. The manual will give the reader background/specifications of the weapon and instructions on its assembly.

Description

The AR-15 carbine/rifle is a .223 Remington/5.56x45mm lightweight air-cooled, gas-operated, magazine-fed, shoulder-fired rifle. The AR-15 is a semi-automatic rifle that fires from a closed bolt. The military M4 variants are either semi-automatic, burst, or full-automatic, which are also closed-bolt systems.

Following are the characteristics of the AR-15 rifle.

AR-15A2 HBAR

CALIBER	.223 Remington or 5.56X45mm NATO
WEIGHT WITHOUT MAGAZINE	8.5 pounds (2.94 kg)
EMPTY 30-ROUND MAGAZINE	0.25 pounds (0.11 kg)
LOADED 30-ROUND MAGAZINE	1 pound (0.45 kg)
OVERALL LENGTH	39 inches (1 meter)
BARREL LENGTH	20 inches (51 cm)
BORE CHARACTERISTICS	Hard chrome-lined; 1:9
METHOD OF OPERATION	Gas-direct system; rotating bolt
MUZZLE VELOCITY	3,200 feet/second (975 meters/second)
EFFECTIVE RANGE	600 meters
FRONT SIGHT	Adjustable front
REAR SIGHT	M16A4 target-style sight adjustable for windage and elevation to 600 meters
SIGHT RADIUS	20 inches (51 cm)
FIRE CONTROL SELECTION	Safe – Semi-automatic
UPPER RECEIVER	Flat top with detachable carrying handle

AR-15A2/A3

CALIBER	.223 Remington or 5.56X45mm NATO
WEIGHT WITHOUT MAGAZINE	7.0 pounds (3.2 kg)
EMPTY 30-ROUND MAGAZINE	0.25 pounds (0.11 kg)
LOADED 30-ROUND MAGAZINE	1 pound (0.45 kg)
LENGTH	29.8 inches to 33 inches (collapsed/extended)
BARREL LENGTH	16.1 inches (41 cm)
BORE CHARACTERISTICS	Hard chrome-lined; 1:7, 1:8, 1:9
METHOD OF OPERATION	Gas-direct system; rotating bolt
MUZZLE VELOCITY	2800 feet/second (884 meters/second)
EFFECTIVE RANGE	600 meters
FRONT SIGHT	Adjustable front
REAR SIGHT	Dual apertures (0-200m and 300-600m) target-style sight adjustable for windage and elevation to 600 meters
SIGHT RADIUS	14.5 inches (37 cm)
FIRE CONTROL SELECTION	Safe – Semi-automatic
UPPER RECEIVER	A2 Model: non-removable carrying handle A3 Model: flat top with detachable carrying handle

SECTION 2

Overview

This manual was developed for individuals wishing to build their own AR-15-type rifle. With the correct tools and basic skills, an individual should be able to safely and competently assemble the necessary parts into a functioning rifle. When in doubt, ask or further research the procedure to prevent making the project more expensive and/or unsafe. Throughout this manual it is assumed that you understand the task prior to starting, and that you maintain a continual assurance of safety. Many common-sense habits will not be repeated every time it is relevant, but will be said up front. It is up to you after that.

Here are some constants to keep in mind throughout this manual:

- Safety - Always remember to wear safety glasses, as pins and springs can cause a hazard with improper installation.

- The work area should be well-lit with plenty of clear and clean workbench space. Place a mat or light-colored towel over your work area to keep parts from rolling around or getting lost.

- The floor area should be taken into consideration, as several small springs and small pins are required for the assembly. If you have a clean floor, it will be easier to find these small parts should they drop. A magnet is helpful in the search for small parts.

- Organize your workspace so you know where items are. Place tools and parts in the order in which you will need them during the assembly.

- Use the correct tool for the specific job.

- Know before you go.

- Accuracy in assembly: almost right is *not right*.

- Prep your parts, tools, and workspace for each task in order to be more efficient.

- Understand the cycle of function of an AR-15 gas system.

- Lubricate where metal-on-metal touch, and where parts move against themselves. Remember that grease will better help items stay in place when installing springs, and lighter oil will be helpful when installing roll pins. Keep these handy on the bench so they are ready during the assembly.

- The appropriate strength of Loctite or similar items must be on hand for use in parts of the assembly.

- Use the receiver vise block and clamp to hold the receiver so you don't need extra hands.

- Specialty tools are a must for some parts of the assembly; use the right tool for the job.

- Before inserting roll pins, slightly collapse the end you are going to insert first so it will start more easily. Needle-nosed pliers can be used, but do not crush the pin; just lightly bend the corners in.

Tools

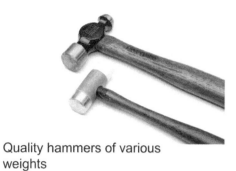

Quality hammers of various weights

Drift punch set

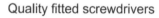

Quality fitted screwdrivers

Roll pin punch set (3/32", 1/8", 5/32")

Armorer's wrench

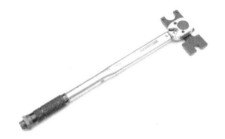

Torque wrench

Upper receiver vise clamp

Vise clamp in use

Lower receiver vise block

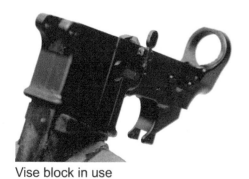

Vise block in use

Barrel vise jaws

Front sight bench block

Tools

Bench block

Flash hider wrench (3/4")

Armorer combo tool

AR-15 bolt ejector tool

Push pin tools

Dry-fire block

Headspace gauges: GO, NO-GO, and FIELD

Loctite® Instructions

Safety Precautions: Keep out of reach of children.

Preparation: Protect work area. Parts to be sealed must be clean and dry. Shake the product thoroughly before use. Note: To prevent the product from clogging in the nozzle, avoid touching the bottle tip to the metal surface.

Application: For threaded through-holes apply several drops of the product onto the bolt at the nut engagement area. For blind holes apply several drops of the product down the internal threads to the bottom of the hole. For sealing applications apply a 360° bead of the product to the leading threads of the male fitting, leaving the first thread free. Force the material into the threads to fill the voids thoroughly. For bigger threads and voids, adjust the product amount accordingly and apply a 360° bead of the product on the female threads as well. Assemble the parts and tighten as required. The product sets in approximately 10 minutes and fully cures in 24 hours.

Cleanup: Clean adhesive residue immediately with a damp cloth. Cured product can be removed with a combination of soaking in methylene chloride or through mechanical abrasion (such as with a wire brush). For disassembly, heat parts up to 482°F (250°C) and separate parts while hot.

Tool List (with part numbers)

The following is a comprehensive list of items needed to perform the work detailed in this book.

DESCRIPTION

Push Pin Tool
Hammer
5/64" Roll Pin Punch
#3 Roll Pin Starter
Lower Receiver Vice Block
Dry Fire Test Block
Trigger Slave Pin
1/4 x 28 Allen Wrench
Flat-Head Screwdriver, Small
1/8" Roll Pin Punch
Wooden Block or Stack of Playing Cards
AR-15 Armorer's Tool
Needle Nose Pliers
AR-15/M16 Front Sight Tool
Rivet tool

DESCRIPTION

3/32" / 2.5mm Roll Pin Punch
Upper Receiver Vice Clamp
Roll Pin Starter Punch #3.5
AR-15 Bolt Ejector Removal Tool
1/16" Roll Pin Punch
Rubbing Alcohol
Boresnake / Cleaning Rod
Q-Tips
Firing Pin Protrusion Gauge
3/32" Hex Wrench
Torque Wrench (35 ft.lb. minimum)
1/8" and 4mm Hex Wrench 3/4" Wrench,
Open-End Headspace gauges

Upper Receiver Torque Values

Compensator (Flash Suppressor)
15 to 20 ft. lbs.

Barrel Nut
30 ft. lbs. minimum, not to exceed 80 ft. lbs. to align the next slot in the barrel nut.

Carrier Key Screws
35 in. lbs. to 40 in. lbs.

Lower Receiver Extension (Buffer Tube)
Rifle: 35 to 39 ft. lbs.

Carbine: Tighten the locking nut to 40 ft. lbs., plus or minus 2 ft. lbs.

Lower Receiver Small Parts

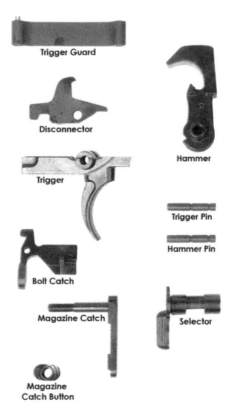

Trigger Guard
Disconnector
Trigger
Bolt Catch
Magazine Catch
Magazine Catch Button
Hammer
Trigger Pin
Hammer Pin
Selector

MIL-SPEC Lower Receiver Small Parts Kit (small parts only)

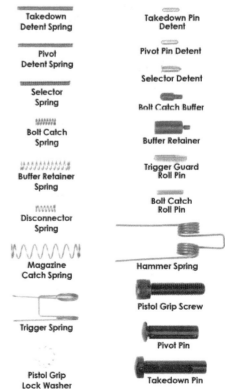

Takedown Detent Spring
Pivot Detent Spring
Selector Spring
Bolt Catch Spring
Buffer Retainer Spring
Disconnector Spring
Magazine Catch Spring
Trigger Spring
Pistol Grip Lock Washer
Takedown Pin Detent
Pivot Pin Detent
Selector Detent
Bolt Catch Buffer
Buffer Retainer
Trigger Guard Roll Pin
Bolt Catch Roll Pin
Hammer Spring
Pistol Grip Screw
Pivot Pin
Takedown Pin

Cycle of Function for an AR-15 Type Rifle

The cycle of operations is a useful tool in understanding and correcting malfunctions because it is the sequence in which malfunctions occur. The sequence starts with a loaded rifle with the selector switch on FIRE.

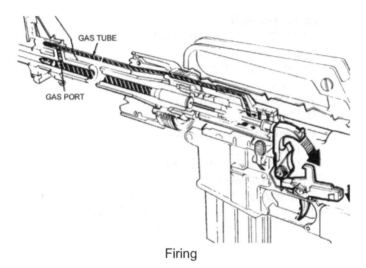

Firing

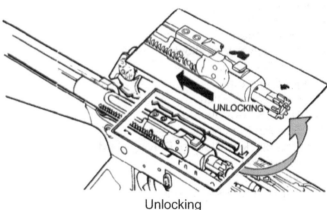

Unlocking

Firing: The trigger is pulled, releasing the hammer, which hits the firing pin, which in turn strikes the primer, which ignites the powder and fires the round.

Unlocking: Gas tapped from the barrel through the gas tube is redirected to the bolt carrier key. This pushes the carrier to the rear and unlocks the bolt from the barrel extension via the cam pin moving in the carrier cam.

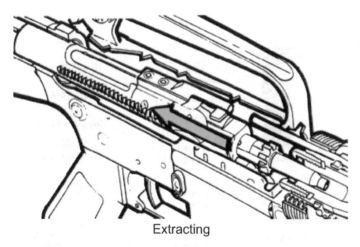

Extracting

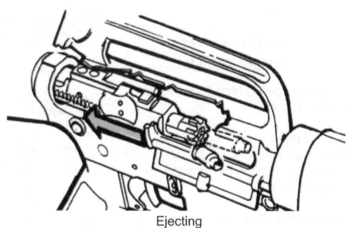

Ejecting

Extracting: The rim of the fired cartridge case is grasped by the claw of the extractor on the ejection port side of the casing while pressure is exerted on the opposite side on the base of the case by the spring-loaded ejector plunger. When the bolt travels to the rear the case is pulled from the chamber.

Ejecting: Once the case is extracted from the chamber and clears the barrel extension, the ejector forcefully pushes the case towards the ejection port as the extractor continues to pull it to the rear. This push-pull of the ejector-extractor expels the case from the rifle.

Cycle of Function for an AR-15 Type Rifle

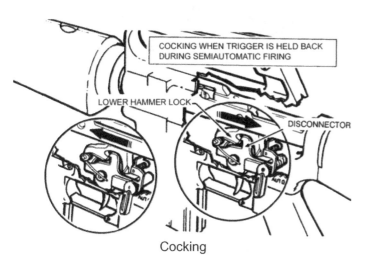

Cocking

Cocking: The bolt and bolt carrier movement to the rear cocks the hammer via the underside of the rear of the carrier.

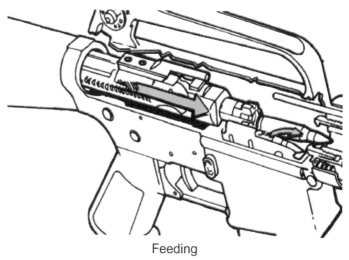

Feeding

Feeding: The bolt and bolt carrier, after moving fully to the rear, come forward (counter recoil) and strip a fresh cartridge from the feed lips of the magazine.

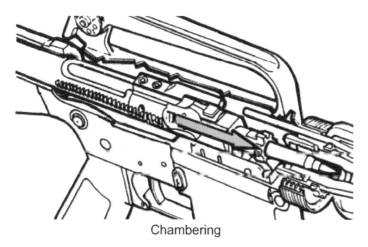

Chambering

Chambering: After stripping a fresh cartridge, the bolt and carrier continue forward, pushing the cartridge up the feed ramps and into the chamber.

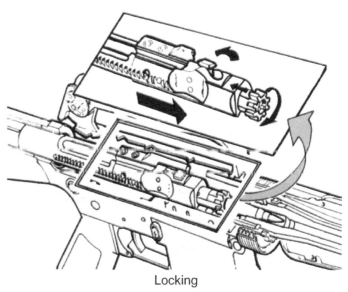

Locking

Locking: The pressure of the action spring pushes the carrier completely forward, and the cam surface engages the cam pin, turning the bolt, locking it into the barrel extension and snapping the extractor around the case rim.

The cycle is now complete and the weapon is ready to fire and return to step one.

Lower Receiver Assembly Parts
Installing the Magazine Catch

Parts needed:
  Lower receiver
  Magazine catch
  Magazine spring
  Magazine button

Tools needed:
  Push pin tool

Stripped lower receiver.

Lower receiver assembly parts.

Magazine catch parts, along with a plastic installation aid.

1) Install the magazine catch into the cutout on the left side of the lower receiver.

2) Hold in the magazine catch.

Lower Receiver Assembly Parts

Installing the Magazine Catch

3) Install the magazine release spring onto the threaded portion of the magazine catch from the right side of the receiver.

4) Insert the magazine release button and screw the button onto the threaded portion of the magazine catch for 3 or 4 turns.

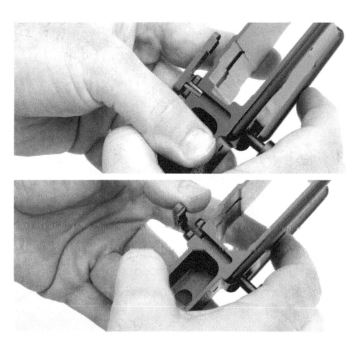

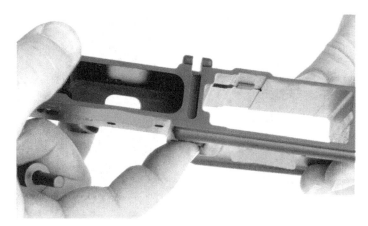

0) Press in on the magazine release button to test the function. Insert a magazine and press the button to release it. There will be some break-in period for the operation to smooth out.

5A) Use a nylon push pin tool, punch, or wooden dowel to push in the magazine release button so you can turn the magazine catch clockwise until the end of the catch is flush with the magazine button head (see 5B).

5B) Final installation of the magazine release button.

Lower Receiver Assembly Parts
Installing the Bolt Catch

Parts needed:
- Bolt catch
- Bolt spring
- Bolt plunger
- Bolt catch roll pin

Tools needed:
- Hammer
- 5/64" roll pin punch or Brownell's bolt catch pin punch
- #3 roll pin starter
- Masking tape
- Lower receiver vise block

Parts required.

Tools required.

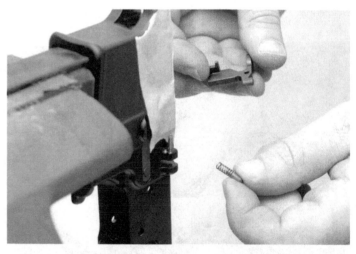

1) Place the lower receiver onto the vise block, which is in the vise. We prefer to do this horizontally (vise block installed horizontally in the vise). Use a piece of masking tape to protect the finish of the receiver from accidental scratches. Start the roll pin into the bolt catch forward hole just enough to hold it, yet not enough to protrude and prevent the catch from being seated.

2) Place a small amount of action lube (or grease) onto the base of the plunger and slide the spring onto it. Insert the spring end into the recess in the receiver with the plunger facing outwards.

Lower Receiver Assembly Parts
Installing the Bolt Catch

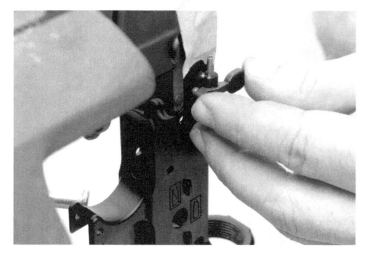

3) Place the bolt catch over the plunger and align with the roll pin hole.

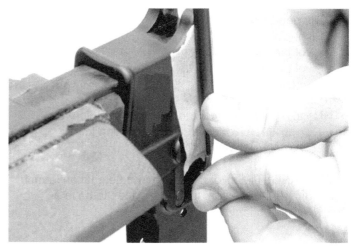

4) While maintaining pressure to hold the bolt catch in alignment in the receiver, place the Brownell's bolt catch roll pin punch onto the roll pin and begin to tap it down so it holds the catch. You may need to reposition the catch as the roll pin comes down to maintain correct alignment. Be careful not to bend the roll pin. If the roll pin is not moving, stop and check to see why.

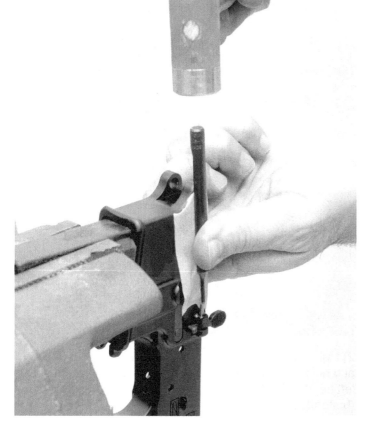

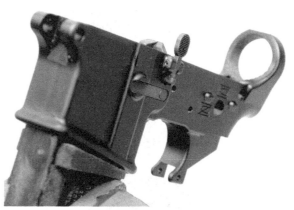

6) Once you have ensured the catch is working properly, continue to seat the roll pin until it is just below the surface of the receiver. You can use a smaller punch to finish seating the pin to avoid marring the receiver finish.

5) Once the roll pin has entered the catch, you may let go and test its function prior to fully seating the roll pin.

Lower Receiver Assembly Parts
Installing the Pivot Pin

Parts needed:
  Pivot pin
  Pivot pin detent spring
  Pivot pin detent

Tools needed:
  None, unless you want to purchase and use a
    Brownell's pivot pin detent installation tool
  Lower receiver vise block

WARNING: The pivot pin spring and detent can launch out during this section. It is a good idea to have a few extras on hand.

Pivot pin, pivot pin detent spring and pivot pin detent.

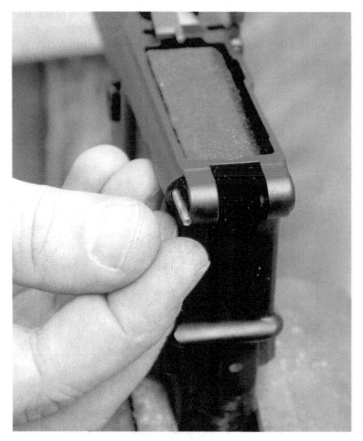

1) Vise up the lower receiver block as shown and place the receiver onto it. Place the pivot pin spring into the hole in the front of the receiver.

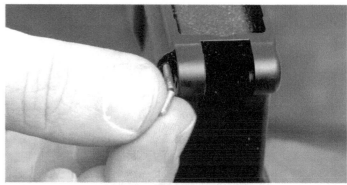

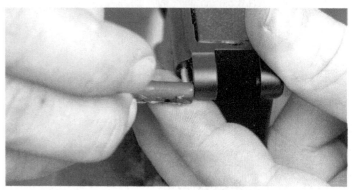

2) Lightly grease the pivot pin. Press in the detent (top) and hold it in alignment with the hole and spring with your left hand while depressing the detent in with the pivot pin (bottom).

Lower Receiver Assembly Parts

Installing the Pivot Pin

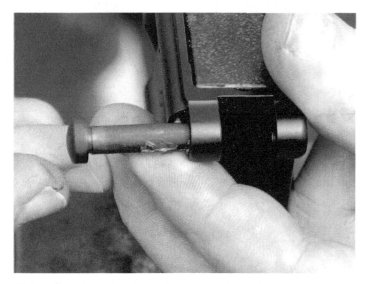

3) As you press the detent into the hole with the pivot pin, slide the pivot pin through the forward pivot pin holes of the receiver. Take your time and perfect your technique.

4) The pivot pin properly installed.

Lower Receiver Assembly Parts

Installing the Geissele SSA Trigger and Hammer

Parts needed:
Geissele Super Semi-Auto (SSA) Trigger
   Springs and pins are included with the trigger package

Tools needed:
   Push pin tool
   Tap hammer
   Dry-fire test block
   Lower receiver vise block
   Trigger slave pin (comes with the Geissele Trigger)

Geissele SSA trigger and hammer with their pins.

NOTE: The trigger assembly has a slave pin installed to hold the disconnector and spring in place. It is replaced by the trigger pin during the assembly process.

1) Begin with your receiver on the receiver vise block (shown chucked into the vise).

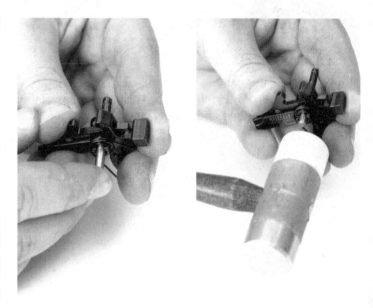

2) Replace the trigger pin in the trigger assembly with the supplied slave pin. You may have to tap it in to force the trigger pin out.

3) Place the trigger assembly down into the receiver through the trigger cutout in the bottom.

4) Ensure your trigger spring legs are forward and protruding through the cutout.

Lower Receiver Assembly Parts

Installing the Geissele SSA Trigger and Hammer

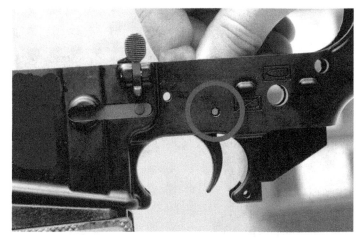

5) Press the trigger assembly down until the slave pin is aligned with the receiver trigger pin hole. You will feel some resistance when the trigger spring compresses.

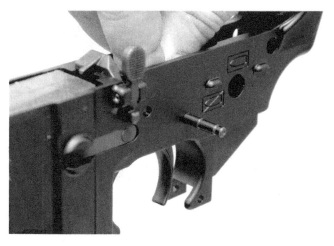

6) While holding the trigger assembly in alignment, place the trigger pin into its hole.

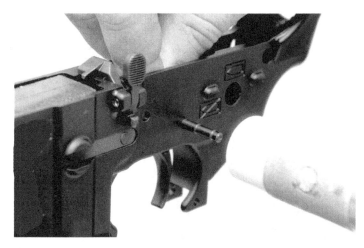

7) Lightly tap the trigger pin to push the slave pin out the far side. If you meet resistance, recheck the alignment.

8) Tap the trigger pin until it is fully inserted into the receiver and the slave pin comes out the far side of the receiver. Check both sides for a flush fit.

9) With the trigger installed, you can now place the hammer and spring into the receiver.

Lower Receiver Assembly Parts
Installing the Geissele SSA Trigger and Hammer

10) Place the hammer spring legs across the top of the trigger pin and rotate the hammer into place, aligning its hole with the hammer holes in the receiver.

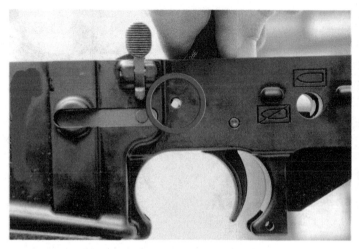

11) Ensure the hammer pin hole is in alignment with the receiver's hammer pin holes.

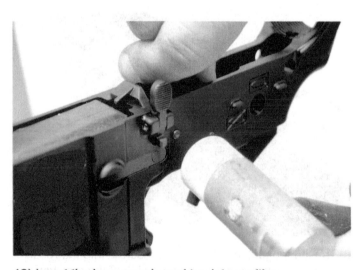

12) Insert the hammer pin and tap into position.

13) Cock the trigger and insert the dry-fire hammer block into the top of the magazine well.

14) Test the first and second stage of the trigger by pressing the trigger until the hammer releases. Recock the hammer as needed to ensure the combo works. First-stage is four pounds of trigger pressure; second-stage is a clean one pound of trigger pressure to fire.

Lower Receiver Assembly Parts

Installing the Geissele SSA Trigger and Hammer

15) Hold the trigger to the rear and recock the hammer to test the reset as you release the trigger. The hammer should/must stay in the cocked position after the trigger is released.

16) Press the trigger again and the hammer should fall.

17) Grease the hammer.

18) Grease the disconnector.

18) The trigger assembly correctly installed and lubricated.

The AR-15 Assembly Guide and Service Manual

Lower Receiver Assembly Parts

Installing the Safety Selector and Stark Pistol Grip

Parts needed:
    AR-15 selector
    Selector detent
    Selector detent spring
    Pistol grip screw, hex ¼-28
    Pistol grip star washer
    Stark pistol grip

Tools needed:
    Allen wrench ¼"-28
    Flathead screwdriver, small
    Lower receiver vise block

Stark pistol grip and safety selector.

1) Insert your lower receiver vise block horizontally in your vise and place your receiver on it with the rear facing up. Place the safety selector into the receiver hole.

2) Place the selector detent into its hole in the bottom of the receiver with the pointed end facing the selector.

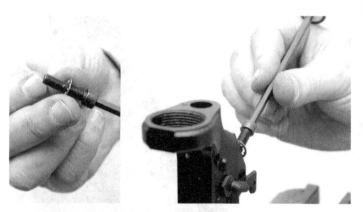

3) Dip the end of the safety detent spring in action lube (not much). This will hold it in the grip for installation. Insert the safety detent spring into the pistol grip.

4) Check the screw's fit to the receiver by placing the star washer on the hex head screw and installing the screw into the receiver. Remove the screw and clean the hole and/or screw as needed.

19

Lower Receiver Assembly Parts

Installing the Safety Selector and Stark Pistol Grip

5) Place a small amount of blue Loctite into the threaded receiver hole.

6) Push the screw into the grip hole.

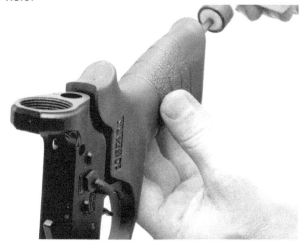

7) Align the grip with the rear of the receiver while aligning the safety detent spring into the detent hole and begin to screw in the hex screw. If you meet resistance, back out and determine why.

8) Continue to check the alignment of the grip as you screw it in. Watch the safety detent spring to ensure it does not kink and that it stays aligned with the detent hole.

9) Do not fully tighten the screw until you have placed the small screw into the front of the trigger guard and have it tight.

Lower Receiver Assembly Parts

Installing the Safety Selector and Stark Pistol Grip

10) Align the front of the trigger guard with the forward trigger pin hole and insert the supplied screw until it is hand-tight, being careful not to strip or over-tighten.

11) Next, hand-tighten the pistol grip screw while maintaining correct alignment. You must have the safety in either the SAFE or FIRE setting for final tightening (see step 12).

12) Check the safety selector for proper function. Place the selector on SAFE and press the trigger (hammer should not fall).

13) Move the selector to FIRE and press the trigger (hammer should fall). **NOTE:** do not let the hammer strike the receiver. Place your thumb against it to prevent this.

Lower Receiver Assembly Parts
Installing the GI Trigger Guard

Parts needed:
  Trigger guard assembly
  Trigger guard roll pin

Tools needed:
  Wood block or stack of playing cards to support the
    receiver at a correct height
  12-ounce ball peen hammer
  Roll pin punch, 1/8"

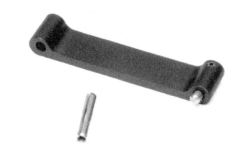

GI trigger guard and roll pin.

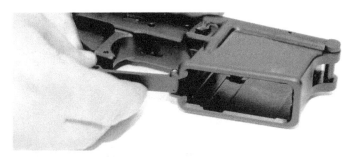

1) Attach the front of the trigger guard assembly to the receiver using the spring-loaded detent. Do this by aligning the front of the trigger guard, as shown, and pressing in the detent.

2) With the trigger guard detent now locking the trigger guard to the receiver, rotate the rear of the trigger guard back into alignment with the receiver holes.

3) With the rear of the trigger guard aligned with the holes in the receiver, lay the receiver on a block of wood or stack of playing cards so the receiver flange is supported to prevent breaking. Lubricate the pin with light machine oil, then start the roll pin into the receiver. While maintaining alignment of the receiver and trigger guard, carefully drive in the pin using the drive pin punch and a 12-oz. hammer.

4) As you tap, ensure that the pin is going straight into the trigger guard holes, as they can become misaligned during this procedure. With the roll pin correctly aligned with the trigger guard holes in the receiver and the rear trigger guard hole, continue to drive in the roll pin until it is flush with the receiver.

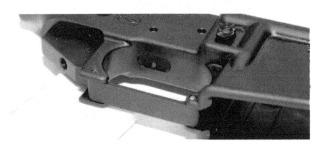

5) The GI trigger guard, properly installed.

Lower Receiver Assembly Parts

Installing the MIL-SPEC Trigger and Hammer

Parts needed:
  Trigger
  Trigger spring
  Trigger pin
  AR-15 disconnector
  AR-15 disconnector spring
  AR-15 hammer
  Hammer spring
  Hammer pin

Tools needed:
  Tap hammer
  Slave pin to hold in the disconnector while installing
  Lower receiver vise block

MIL-SPEC trigger and hammer with their pins.

NOTE: the trigger assembly has a slave pin installed to hold the disconnector and spring in place.

1) Begin with your receiver on the receiver vise block, which is chucked into the vise. Assemble the trigger assembly and hold it together with a slave pin. Place the trigger assembly down into the receiver through the trigger cutout in the bottom.

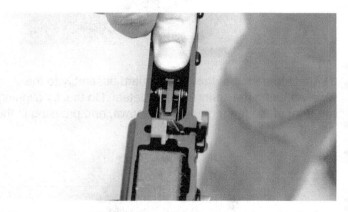

2) Ensure your trigger spring legs are forward and out of this cutout.

3) Press the trigger down against the spring tension of the trigger spring to align the slave pin with the receiver trigger pin hole.

4) With the trigger assembly held in alignment, place the trigger pin into its hole and tap it through. If you meet resistance, recheck the alignment.

Lower Receiver Assembly Parts

Installing the MIL-SPEC Trigger and Hammer

5) Tap the trigger pin until it drives out the slave pin and it is evenly inserted into the receiver. Check both sides.

6) The trigger pin correctly installed.

7) With the trigger installed, you can now place the hammer and spring into the receiver.

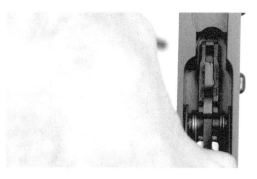

8) Place the hammer spring legs across the top of the trigger pin and rotate the hammer into place, aligning its hole with the hammer pin holes in the receiver.

9) Ensure the hammer pin hole is in alignment with the receiver's hammer pin holes.

10) Insert the hammer pin and, while maintaining alignment, tap the pin until it is centered in the receiver.

11) When correctly installed, the spring legs will be in the position shown.

12) Insert the dry-fire hammer block into the top of the magazine well. Test the trigger. Recock the hammer as needed to ensure the combo works. Either using the hammer block or your thumb to block the hammer, pull the trigger. The hammer should fall. Hold the trigger to the rear and recock the hammer to test the reset as you release the trigger.

Lower Receiver Assembly Parts

Installing the Safety Selector and A2 Pistol Grip

Parts needed:
  AR-15 selector
  Selector detent
  Selector spring
  Pistol grip screw, hex ¼-28
  Pistol grip star washer
  A2 pistol grip

Tools needed:
  Allen wrench ¼"-28
  Lower receiver vise block

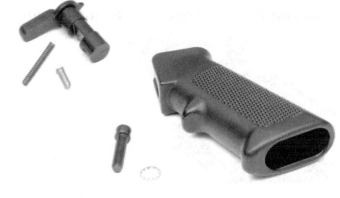

Safety selector and A2 grip components.

1) Reposition the receiver vise block so the front of the receiver is facing down. Insert the safety selector into the receiver's left side.

2) Insert the safety lever detent (point forward) into the bottom of the right side of the receiver.

3) Dip the safety lever detent spring in some action lube or grease and insert it into the hole on the right side of the pistol grip. The grease will keep the spring from falling out of the grip during assembly.

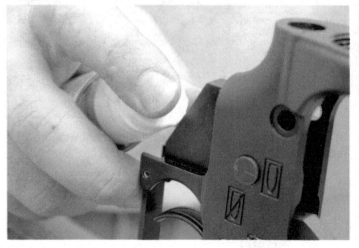

4) Place a small amount of Loctite (blue) in the threads in the pistol grip screw hole of the receiver.

Lower Receiver Assembly Parts

Installing the Safety Selector and A2 Pistol Grip

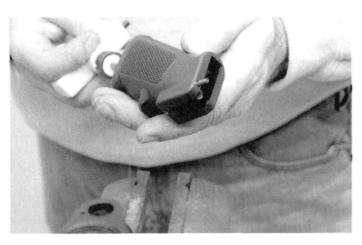

5) Place the star washer onto the pistol grip screw; place the screw on the appropriate hex wrench and through the pistol grip.

6) Position the pistol grip so the grip screw aligns with the receiver's grip screw hole, then carefully start the screw. Maintain proper alignment of the detent spring into the detent hole.

7) Ensure that the screw is at the correct angle so it will easily screw in and not strip the aluminum receiver's threads. It is advisable to pre-check that the screw fits in the hole prior to final assembly.

8) As you tighten the grip screw, continue to align the pistol grip, with emphasis on aligning the safety detent spring with the bottom of the safety detent.

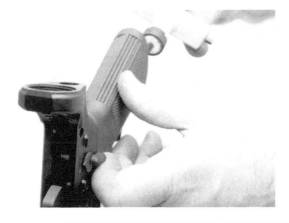

9) When you get to the point where the screw is tightening, ensure that the safety lever is in the FIRE position for final tightening. Do not over-tighten.

Lower Receiver Assembly Parts
Installing the Stock

Parts needed:
    Buffer tube, MIL-SPEC six-position
    Carbine stock latch plate
    Carbine stock lock ring with notches
    Carbine buffer spring
    Carbine buffer
    Buffer retainer
    Buffer retainer spring
    Stock, Magpul CTR
    -or-
    Stock, MIL-SPEC

Tools needed:
    Multipurpose AR-15 armorer's tool
    Lower receiver vise block

The CTR collapsible buttstock assembly, parts, and tools.

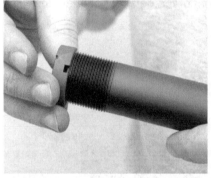

1) Start the castle nut onto the buffer tube with the tightening notches towards the rear of the tube until it is fully on.

2) Next, slide on the buttstock latch plate with the locking nub (arrow) facing the front of the buffer tube. Align the stock plate key with the cutout on the bottom of the buffer tube and slide it fully onto the tube.

3) With the receiver horizontally secured in the vise with the vise block, apply an anti-seize on the buffer tube hole's threads.

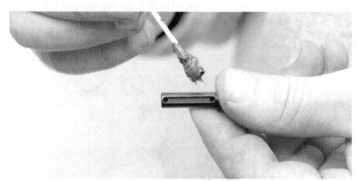

4) Apply action lube or grease to the take-down pin.

Lower Receiver Assembly Parts

Installing the Stock

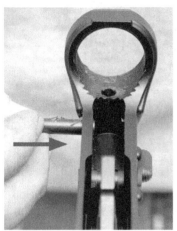 

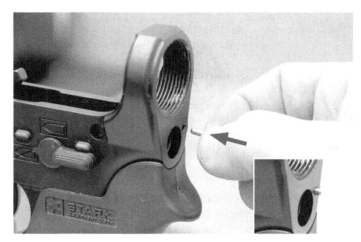

5) Fully insert the take-down pin into the take-down pin hole of the receiver on the right side, orientating the notch in the pin to the rear of the receiver. This notch is what the take-down pin detent will align and capture the pin with when the buttstock locking plate is on.

6) Insert the take-down pin detent into the small hole on the right side of the rear of the receiver and press it completely in. Both ends of the pin are the same.

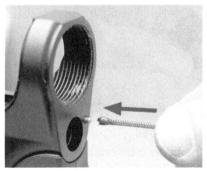 

7) Dip the take-down pin detent spring into some action lube or grease and insert it behind the take-down pin detent.

8) Start threading the buffer tube onto the receiver while keeping the buttstock locking plate to the rear as you thread it on. Make sure the detent pin spring does not fall out or get kinked.

9) Continue to thread on the buffer tube until you begin to near the buffer pin retainer hole. Notice that the end of the buffer tube has an extended part to hold in the buffer retainer.

10) With the buffer tube shy of the buffer retainer hole, place the buffer retainer spring into the buffer retainer and insert both of them into the buffer retainer hole, spring first.

Lower Receiver Assembly Parts

Installing the Stock

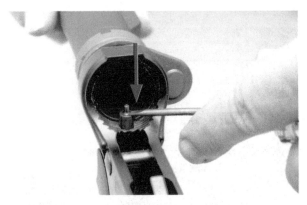

11) With the buffer retainer pressed down with a screw driver or finger, continue to thread on the buffer tube until the extended piece on the tube retains the buffer retainer.

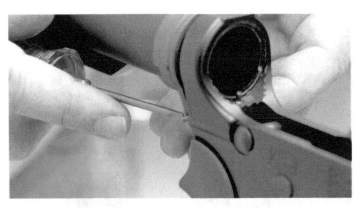

12) Once the buffer retainer is held by the buffer tube, you can press in the take-down detent spring so you can align the buttstock locking plate.

 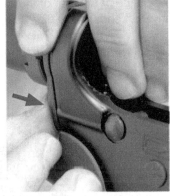

13) With the take-down detent spring straight and against the buttstock locking plate, push the plate forward and hold it in this position.

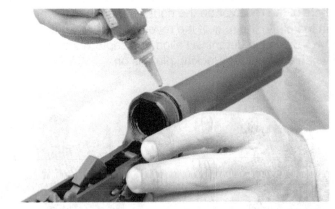

14) While holding the buttstock locking plate forward, apply some Loctite (blue) onto the buffer tube threads prior to tightening down the castle nut. Hand-tighten the castle nut.

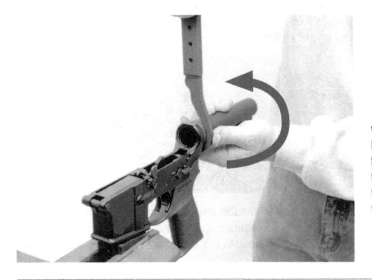

15) Once the castle nut is hand-tight, use your stock wrench to finish tightening the nut. Do not over tighten. Ensure the stock wrench is properly and fully seated into the notch of the castle nut, being careful not to damage the castle nut with excessive tightening. You may choose to stake the castle nut with the buttstock locking plate, but that is up to you.

Lower Receiver Assembly Parts

Installing the Stock

16) Slide the buttstock onto the buffer tube.

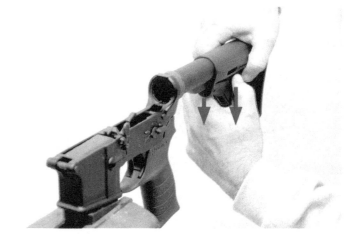

17) Once you have started the buffer tube, unlock the stock's mechanism for adjusting the length of pull to slide the stock further onto the buffer tube. The Magpul CTR has a cross-pin, which you must pull down to advance the buttstock forward.

18) Test the collapsible stock in different positions for correct function.

19) Prior to inserting the buffer spring and buffer, lightly lubricate the inside of the buffer tube.

20) Insert the buffer into the buffer spring, then start the spring into the buffer tube.

21) Fully seat the buffer into the tube, ensuring that the buffer retainer pin holds the buffer in the tube.

Lower Receiver Assembly Parts

Installing the Stock

22) The completely assembled lower receiver.

23) To mate the lower receiver to an upper receiver, first pull out on the take-down and pivot pins. Next, align the upper and lower receivers, then press in on the pivot pin (front, arrow) until it is fully seated.

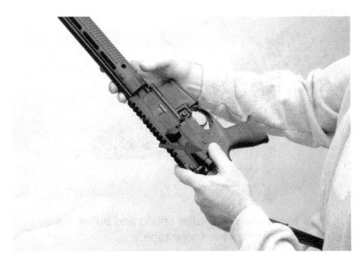

24) Next, press in on the take-down pin until it is fully seated.

25) The rifle is now fully assembled.

Upper Receiver Options

Here are several types of stripped upper receivers, each with different features for different applications.

AR-15 A1 Upper Receiver

The AR-15 A1 has a fixed carry handle and shell deflector, and requires the installation of the forward assist assembly, ejection port cover assembly, and the A1 sight assembly that allows only for windage adjustment. This upper is ideal to build a civilian version of the Vietnam-era M-16 Rifle.

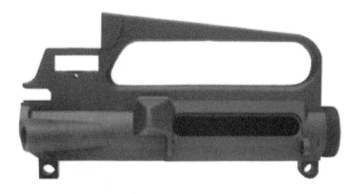

AR-15 A2 Upper Receiver

The AR-15 A2 has a fixed carry handle and shell deflector, and requires the installation of the forward assist assembly, ejection port cover assembly, and the A2 sight assembly that allows for windage and elevation adjustments. This is a popular upper to use for building a rifle for use in shooting matches.

AR-15 A3 Upper Receiver

The AR-15 A3 has a flat top with a Picatinny rail and shell deflector, and requires the installation of the forward assist assembly and ejection port cover assembly. This is the current military upper, and is used to build a civilian copy of the M4 (carbine with 16" barrel) or M-16 A4 (rifle with 20" barrel). It's also great for building any type of varmint or target carbine/rifle since any type of optic can be mounted to the Picattiny rail.

AR-15 Flat Top Upper Receiver

The AR-15 Flattop has many configurations for the upper receiver, with various heights of Picatinny rails for mounting scopes. These generally do not accommodate the forward assists or ejection port cover assemblies, and are also known as the "slick-sided" uppers. The flattop is great for building any type of varmint or target carbine/rifle since any type of optic can be mounted to the Picatinny rail.

Upper Receiver Assembly Parts

NOTE: At the end of each part of the process you should test the component for proper function before moving to the next step. This may require lubricant and/or repetitive manipulation to break the parts in, as they are new and tight.

Upper receiver components.

Upper Receiver Assembly Parts

Installing the Ejection Port Cover

Parts needed:
    Upper receiver
    Ejection port cover
    Ejection port cover pin
    Ejection port cover pin "C" clip
    Ejector port cover spring

Tools needed:
    Needle-nose pliers
    Patience

The stripped upper receiver and ejection port parts (ejection port, ejection port spring, ejection port rod, and "C" snap ring).

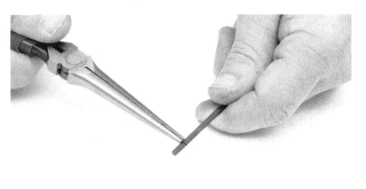

1) Use needle-nose pliers to place the "C" snap ring onto the ejection port cover pin. Pinch the midpoint on the snap ring and press it into the groove of the ejection port rod until it snaps into place.

2) Lay the left side of the receiver onto your working surface. Hold the ejection port cover and insert the end of the ejection port rod without the snap ring into the hole on the front of the receiver and through the first part of the cover.

3) Press the rod in until it extends through the middle of the cover approximately a quarter-inch.

4) Start the long leg end of the ejection port spring onto the rod.

Upper Receiver Assembly Parts
Installing the Ejection Port Cover

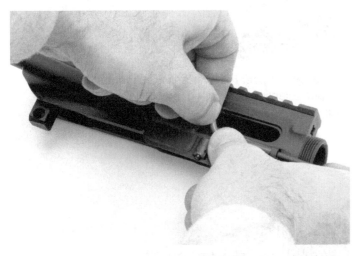

5) This is where some technique and dexterity come into play, and you will just have to work it until you get it right. While holding the spring onto the rod with your right hand, twist the short tail end of the spring down while tensioning the spring by turning that short tail to orient it to the top of the receiver.

6) Once you have the spring tensioned up, it can be held against the receiver to maintain this position while you push the ejection port rod further into position and into the rear hole in the receiver.

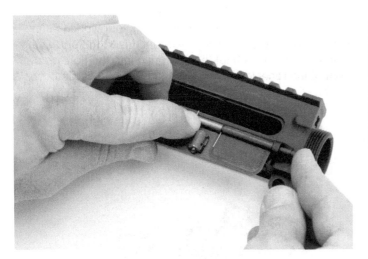

7) Fully seat the rod into the rear hole of the receiver.

8) Now you can let go and test the operation of the spring-loaded ejection port cover.

Upper Receiver Assembly Parts

Installing the Forward Assist

Parts needed:
   Forward assist
   Forward assist spring
   Forward assist roll pin

Tools needed:
   Tap hammer
   Roll pin punch 1/8" - installation
   Roll pin punch 3.32"/2.5mm - removal
   Upper receiver vise clamp
   Roll pin starter punch #3S

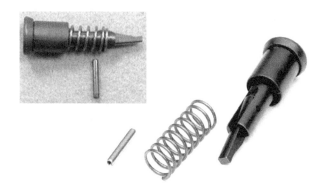

Forward assist parts: roll pin, forward assist spring, and forward assist.

1) Place the upper receiver in the vise clamps and into the vise so your work is being held firmly in place. Some start the pin from the top and some from the bottom (we'll illustrate going from the top). You may also tape around the receiver if you feel you might scratch it from a slipped punch. Regardless, take your time. Lightly lube the roll pin with light machine oil and start the pin in with light taps from the hammer.

2) Once the roll pin is started you can place the spring (it does not matter which end) onto the forward assist and press it into the receiver. Orient it so that the cutout on the side of the forward assist is on the left side, allowing the pin to pass by and retain the spring-loaded assembly. Hold in the forward assist and tap.

3) While maintaining inward pressure on the forward assist to hold it in, tap down the roll pin far enough to engage the spring-loaded assembly. The roll pin will now hold in the assembly. You can now check its function by pushing it in and ensuring that it springs back.

4) Now continue to seat the roll pin until it is slightly below the surface of the receiver. You may use a smaller punch to ensure it is subsurface without marring the receiver finish.

Upper Receiver Assembly Parts

Checking for Proper (SAFE) Headspace on a Rifle Barrel and Bolt

Parts needed:
  "GO" gauge (appropriate caliber for chamber)
    5.56x45
  "NO GO" gauge (appropriate caliber for chamber)
    5.56x45
  "FIELD" gauge (appropriate caliber for chamber)
    5.56x45
  Bolt to be used with the barrel

Tools needed:
  AR-15 bolt ejector removal tool
  Tap hammer
  Roll pin punch 5/64" - install
  Roll pin punch 1/16" - removal
  Alcohol
  Boresnake or cleaning rod with brush and patches
  Q-Tips

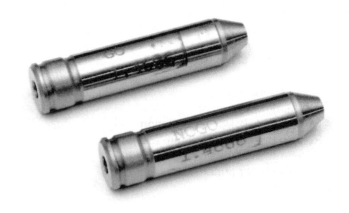

All weapons that fire a cartridge have headspace, and an improper fit can damage the weapon and injure the shooter. Do not switch bolts into different rifles without first checking headspace.

Headspace is the distance between the face of the breech (bolt face) and the base (back of the case, i.e. the primer area) of the cartridge when the action is closed. This distance is measured in thousandths of an inch.

While a small amount of headspace (.001 to .003) is permissible for most standard cartridges to allow the action to close when there is a small amount of dirt or grit, excessive headspace can be very dangerous and can impair accuracy.

When a rifle is fired, the powder burns, creating gas pressure. The brass case expands against the walls of the chamber under extreme pressure, thus preventing the gases from venting into the action and blowing into the shooter's face. The rapidly expanding gases try to escape from the case and, therefore, push the bullet down the bore as the only means of escape. But we know that "for every action there is an equal and opposite reaction." So, this same amount of pressure that is pushing on the bullet is also pushing on the rear (head) of the brass case.

If the rifle has "excessive headspace" (more than factory specifications for that cartridge) then, when fired, as the case clings to the chamber walls under pressure, the case will stretch in the rear unsupported area just forward of the "head" and split, allowing massive amounts of gas under extreme pressure to infiltrate the action and blast rearward like rocket exhaust back at the shooter. This situation is

obviously a potentially dangerous one that could result in the destruction of the firearm along with injury or death to the shooter.

How do you measure for proper headspace?

The use of a "headspace gauge" is the most reliable way to test the length and depth of a rifle chamber. These gauges are made of steel and are ground to precise dimensions to replicate the length of a specific cartridge plus the additional distance to the breech face, thereby giving you an overall length or "headspace."

Important Guidelines for Measuring Headspace

• If a rifle closes on a GO gauge, the rifle chamber will accept any ammunition that is made within S.A.A.M.I. (Sporting Arms and Ammunition Manufacturers' Institute) specifications. This is acceptable as long as the overall condition of the firearm is safe. The bolt closing on a GO gauge eliminates any possibility of the chamber being too short.

• If a rifle closes on a NO GO gauge, then the rifle chamber might have excessive headspace. It needs to be inspected and measured more carefully. Most gunsmiths chamber a rifle's headspace between the GO and NO GO dimensions.

• If a rifle closes on a FIELD (reject) gauge, the rifle chamber is dangerously close to or already over the S.A.M.M.I. specified maximum chamber size, and it should not be used until headspace is corrected.

Upper Receiver Assembly Parts

Checking for Proper (SAFE) Headspace on a Rifle Barrel and Bolt

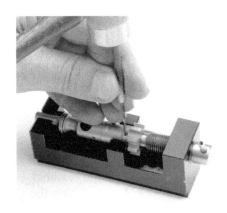

1) Remove the extractor from the bolt by pushing out the extractor retaining pin with a small punch. Once this pin is removed the extractor should fall away from the bolt.

The ejector is removed from the bolt by using an ejector removal tool. This tool will depress the spring-loaded ejector while you use a punch to drive out the retaining pin.

2) With the bolt in the ejector removal tool, use a small (1/16" No. 1) punch to tap out the ejector retaining pin. Once this pin is out of the bolt, remove the bolt from the tool and pull out the ejector. You will not need to pull out the ejector spring. Thoroughly clean the bolt face. The photo at right shows the ejector removed from the bolt.

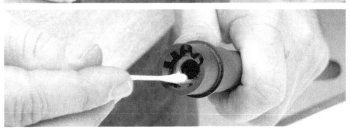

3) Thoroughly clean the barrel extension and chamber of the barrel to be headspace-checked with alcohol (top) and a swab (bottom) to remove any oils.

4) Insert the GO gauge (top). Insert the bolt into the barrel extension (bottom). The bolt should lock into battery without a lot of pressure (into battery is the configuration when the rifle will fire a live round and the GO gauge is dimensioned to represent a live S.A.A.M.I. spec'd cartridge). If the GO gauge does not lock into battery, you may need to try another bolt or another barrel, as the barrel extensions are factory installed. If your bolt locks into battery, you will now check with your NO GO gauge, which should not lock into battery.

Upper Receiver Assembly Parts

Checking for Proper (SAFE) Headspace on a Rifle Barrel and Bolt

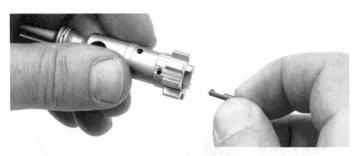

5) Once your bolt is checked for headspace and is within tolerances, you can reassemble your bolt by inserting the ejector into the ejector hole, which already contains the ejector spring, with the cutout in the ejector towards the center of the bolt. This cutout allows the retaining pin to hold the ejector in the bolt while it is tensioned with the ejector spring.

7) Look through the ejector retaining pin hole to ensure that your pin will properly hold the ejector in. If the orientation is incorrect, you will not see light through the hole and you must reorient the ejector.

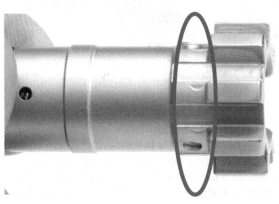

9) Check the far side to ensure that the pin is centered. The retaining pin should not protrude from either side of the bolt.

6) With the ejector reinserted into the bolt in the correct orientation, place the bolt back in the ejector removal tool and apply tension to the ejector.

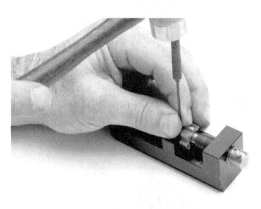

8) Once you have made sure the hole is clear, you can tap in the ejector retaining pin and set it below the surface.

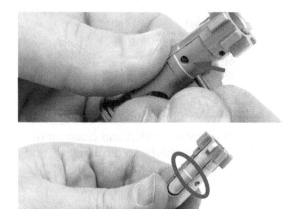

10) To finish the bolt reassembly, push the extractor back into place and reinsert the extractor retaining pin (top). Ensure that the retaining pin does not protrude from either side of the bolt (bottom).

Upper Receiver Assembly Parts

Assembling the Bolt Carrier Group

Parts needed:
- Bolt assembly
- Bolt carrier with gas key installed
- Bolt cam pin
- Firing pin
- Firing pin retaining pin

Tools needed:
- Firing pin protrusion gauge

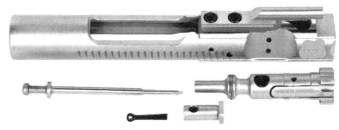

The bolt carrier group.

NOTE: Various types of bolt carrier groups are available, and all should come complete as shown.

1) Insert the bolt into the bolt carrier.

2) Ensure the extractor on the bolt is to the right and align the hole in the carrier with the hole in the bolt.

3) Insert the cam pin as shown. It goes in only one way.

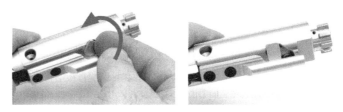

4) Turn the cam pin 90 degrees (left). At right is the cam pin in the correct orientation.

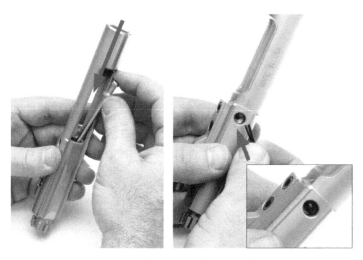

5) Turn the carrier to a "bolt-down" orientation and insert the firing pin (left). With the firing pin fully inserted, insert the firing pin retaining pin (right). The firing pin retaining pin is shown correctly installed in the inset photo.

6) To check the firing pin protrusion with the min/max gauge, push the bolt to the rear so the firing pin is exposed through the face of the bolt. The firing pin should hit the "minimum" gauge slot when the gauge is passed over the pin. The pin should not contact the "maximum gauge slot when the gauge is passed over it.

Upper Receiver Assembly Parts

Assembling the Gas System: Samson Gas Block

Parts needed:
 Samson low-pro ile gas block
 Gas tube roll pin
 Gas tube (appropriate length for barrel)
 • Carbine-length
 • Mid-length
 • Ri le-length

Tools needed:
 Hex wrench 3/32"
 Bench block
 Tap hammer
 Roll pin punch

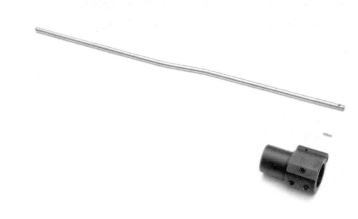

Gas system parts.

1) Remove the 3/32" hex screws from the block (left). Clean the screw holes in the gas block with a Q-Tip dipped in alcohol (right), which will degrease the holes for a better bond with the Loctite.

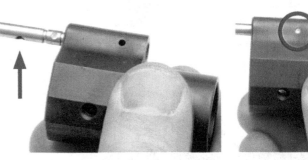

2) Insert the gas tube with the correct orientation for the gas hole in the tube (left). Ensure the alignment is correct for the insertion of the gas tube roll pin (right).

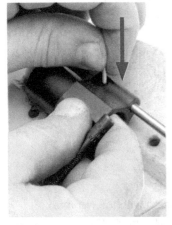 

3) Support the gas block on a bench block as shown. Insert the gas tube roll pin (left). Seat the roll pin (right).

4) The correctly pinned gas tube on the gas block.

Upper Receiver Assembly Parts
Assembling the Upper Receiver Parts

NOTICE: If you are assembling a MIL-SPEC upper receiver, proceed to page 46.

Parts needed:
  Barrel
  Barrel nut
  Gas block installed on the gas tube

Tools needed:
  Upper receiver vise clamp
  Torque wrench (35 ft. lbs. at a minimum)
  Barrel nut wrench
  3/32" hex wrench

1) Insert the upper receiver block into the upper receiver, close the ejection port cover, then place the receiver into the receiver vise clamp and into the vise as shown.

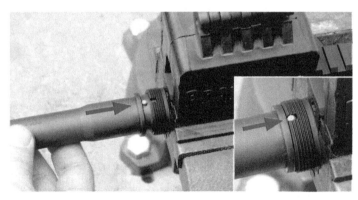

2) Slide the barrel extension into the receiver and align the pin on the barrel with the cutout in the receiver. Inset photo shows the barrel properly seated in the receiver.

3) Apply a small amount of anti-seize onto the receiver threads.

4) Carefully slide the barrel nut down the barrel with the threads first and begin to tighten down the nut.

5) Set your torque wrench to a minimum of 35 foot-pounds. Maximum torque is around 80 foot-pounds.

Upper Receiver Assembly Parts

Assembling the Upper Receiver Parts

6) Place the barrel nut wrench onto the torque wrench as shown, then align the wrench pins onto the barrel nut, ensuring you fully seat the wrench onto the nut. Note the orientation of the wrench. This orientation allows for an accurate torque. If the wrench is off the end of the barrel nut wrench, the torque will be more than desired.

7) As you torque, hopefully the barrel nut will align with the gas tube hole in the receiver as shown. If it does not do so at the minimum poundage, you may work up to a maximum of 80 foot-pounds, or use a Dremel tool to remove the tooth that is in the way of the gas tube. Do not allow the gas tube to come in contact with the barrel nut.

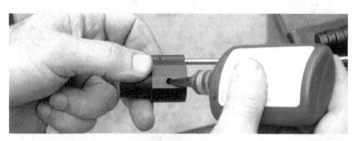

8) Prepare the Samson gas block and gas tube for installation by removing the hex socket screws (4) and putting a drop of red Loctite into the screw holes.

9) Slide the gas block/gas tube onto the barrel and align it with the hole in the front of the upper receiver. Also align the gas block over the gas port on the top of the barrel (inset photo).

10) The gas block is shown fully seated on the barrel.

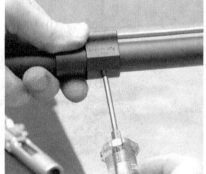

11) Check for proper alignment of the gas block over the gas port (left). Next, hold the gas block, insert the gas block screws, and tighten the block with a 3/32" hex wrench (right).

Upper Receiver Assembly Parts
Installing the APEX Free-Float Handguard System

Parts needed:
APEX Handguard System
- Carbine-length
- Ri le length

Tools needed:
Hex wrenches (1/8" and 4mm)

The Handguard System.

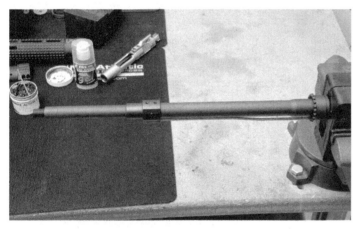

1) Vise up the upper receiver with the receiver clamps so the gas tube is oriented down.

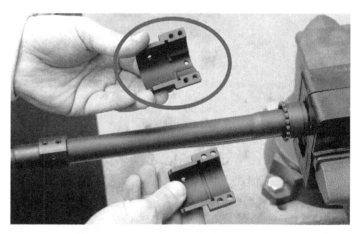

2) Separate the handguard clamps and note which goes on top. The top clamp (top) has a cutout for the gas tube.

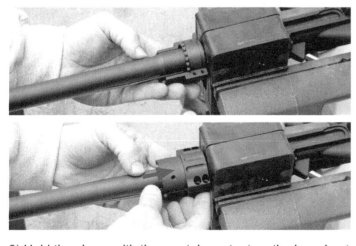

3) Hold the clamp with the gas tube cutout on the barrel nut at the bottom of the assembly (top). Place the other clamp on top of the barrel nut (bottom). Align the cutout on the clamp with the front of the receiver so that the hand guard will align with the front of the receiver and the gas block.

4) Place a small amount of anti-seize into the screw holes and start the longer of the four socket hex head screws through the clamp.

Upper Receiver Assembly Parts

Installing the APEX Free-Float Forearm System

5) Check the left and right spacing between the clamps, ensuring that they are even.

6) Finish tightening the four screws, one side at a time, to maintain the alignment. Do not over tighten.

7) Start the handguard tube over the barrel with the four mounting holes to the rear. Note that the logo is up for proper orientation.

8) Align the holes in the tube with the screw holes in the clamps.

9) Apply a small amount of anti-seize into the screw holes and start the four shorter screws that secure the tube. Do not tighten until all four are started, and do not over tighten. It is best to put your accessory rails onto the tube prior to putting the tube onto the clamps.

Upper Receiver Assembly Parts

Assembling the MIL-SPEC Upper Receiver

Parts needed:
 M4 cut barrel
 Handguard retainer lange
 Delta ring
 Barrel nut
 Delta ring spring
 Retaining ring
 Sling rivet
 Front sight post set screw
 Front sight post detent spring
 Front sight post detent
 Front sight post
 F-Marked sight post frame
 Gas tube roll pin
 Sling swivel
 Gas Tube
 • Carbine-length
 • Mid-length
 • Rifle-length

Handguards
 • Carbine-length
 • Mid-length
 • Ri le-length

Tools needed:
 AR-15/M16 front sight tool
 Front sight bench block
 Upper receiver vise clamp
 Torque wrench (35 ft. lbs at a minimum)
 Barrel nut wrench or AR-15/M16 armorer's tool
 Tap hammer
 Roll pin punch
 Hex wrench (3/32")
 Rivet tool

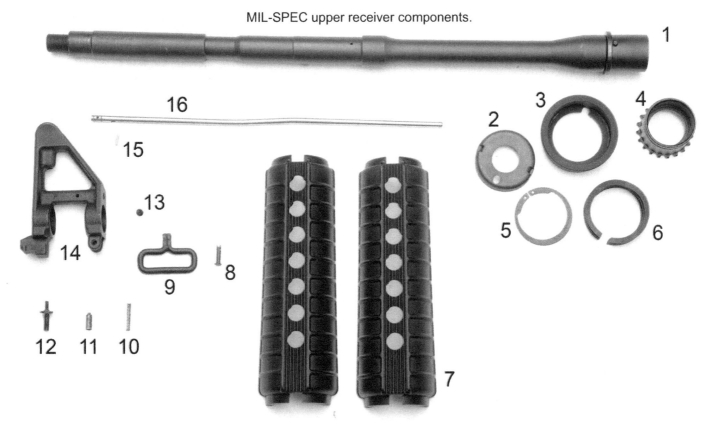

MIL-SPEC upper receiver components.

1) M4 cut barrel	5) Retaining ring	9) Sling swivel	13) Front sight post set screw
2) Handguard retainer flange	6) Delta ring spring	10) Front sight post detent spring	14) F-Marked sight post frame
3) Delta ring	7) Handguard	11) Front sight post detent	15) Gas tube roll pin
4) Barrel nut	8) Sling rivet	12) Front sight post	16) Gas tube

Upper Receiver Assembly Parts
Assembling the MIL-SPEC Upper Receiver

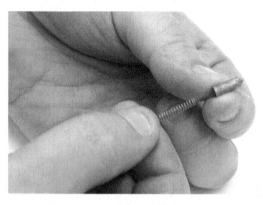

1) Insert the front sight post detent spring into the front sight post detent.

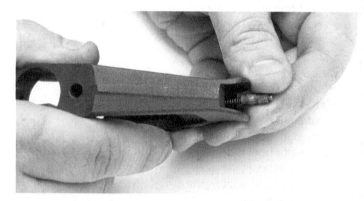

2) Insert the front sight post detent and spring assembly into its recess in the front of the sight post frame.

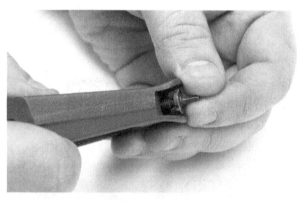

3) Begin screwing the front sight post into the sight post frame until the detent restricts further rotation.

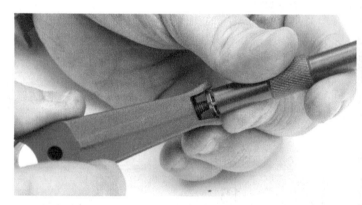

4) Use the AR-15/M16 front sight post tool to screw the sight post the rest of the way into the frame. The legs of the tool fit into the sight post recesess and prevent the detent from interrupting the rotation.

5) Rotate the sight post until it is flush in the frame as shown. The sight post can be adjusted up or down to later zero the rifle using the sight post tool.

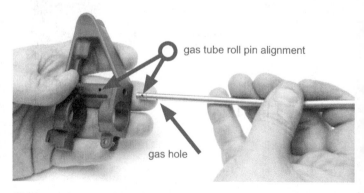

gas tube roll pin alignment

gas hole

6) Insert the gas tube with the correct orientation for the gas hole in the tube. Ensure the alignment is correct for the insertion of the gas tube roll pin.

Upper Receiver Assembly Parts

Assembling the MIL-SPEC Upper Receiver

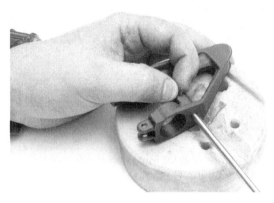

7) Using the bench block as shown, insert the gas tube roll pin.

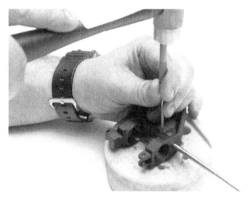

8) Seat the roll pin into the frame by tapping it flush into the frame with a punch.

9) Insert the barrel nut through the small diameter end of the Delta ring as shown.

10) Insert the Delta ring spring over the barrel nut and between the Delta ring as shown.

11) The assembly is held together with the retaining ring. Start the retaining ring over the barrel nut and, using a flathead screwdriver or snap ring pliers, snap the ring into place in the barrel nut retaining groove.

12) Use a punch or similar tool to align the retaining ring, spring, and Delta ring to make an open passageway for the gas tube to be inserted through the assembly.

Upper Receiver Assembly Parts
Assembling the MIL-SPEC Upper Receiver

13) The Delta ring and barrel nut assembly properly aligned.

14) Refer to pg. 42, steps 1-3 for installing the barrel onto the receiver. Next, screw the Delta ring assembly onto the barrel as shown, trying not to disturb the component alignment.

15) Use an AR-15/M16 armorer's wrench or a barrel nut wrench to finish snugging the assembly onto the barrel.

16) Set your torque wrench to a minimum of 35 foot-pounds (maximum torque is around 80 foot-pounds). Seat the wrench pins fully onto the barrel nut and torque to within the specs. Note the proper orientation of the torque wrench for accurate torque application.

17) Realign the Delta ring components to open a slot for the gas tube by using a punch. If the teeth of the barrel nut block the gas tube channel, continue torquing the nut (but do not exceed 80 foot-pounds!) until the channel is clear.

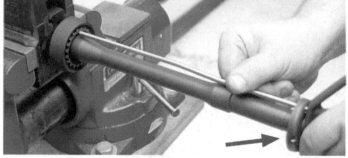

18) Install the handguard retainer flange onto the gas tube (arrow), then install the gas tube/sight frame/handguard retainer flange assembly onto the barrel as shown. Check that the gas tube will insert freely through the Delta ring assembly and into the receiver. If not, adjust the barrel nut. Do not allow the gas tube to come in contact with the barrel nut. This photo shows the barrel nut blocking the gas tube.

Upper Receiver Assembly Parts

Assembling the MIL-SPEC Upper Receiver

19) Once the Delta ring assembly is properly aligned to accept the gas tube, push the assembly fully onto the barrel and into the upper receiver. When correctly seated, the handguard retainer flange will sit flush against the cut in the M4 barrel.

20) Install the front sight post set screw into the bottom of the sight post frame. A slight detent in the barrel accepts the set screw, which prevents the sight post frame from twisting on the barrel. (SEE SIDEBAR BELOW IF YOU ARE INSTALLING A TRADITIONAL GAS BLOCK.)

NOTE: ALTERNATIVE GAS BLOCK INSTALLATION PROCEDURE

If you want to install a traditional gas block using tapered roll pins, the gas block and barrel must be drilled as a unit. This is a procedure that should be performed only by a qualified gunsmith.

Once the roll pin holes have been drilled through the gas block and barrel, place the assembly on a bench block and tap the tapered roll pins into place to secure the gas block to the barrel.

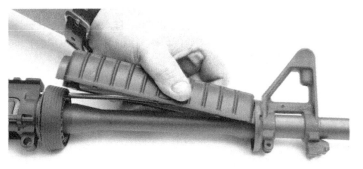

21) Insert the top half of the handguard assembly into the handguard retainer flange.

22) Pull back on the Delta ring and maneuver the rear of the handguard onto the front of the Delta ring. Snap the upper handguard section downward so that it is captured by the Delta ring.

Upper Receiver Assembly Parts
Assembling the MIL-SPEC Upper Receiver

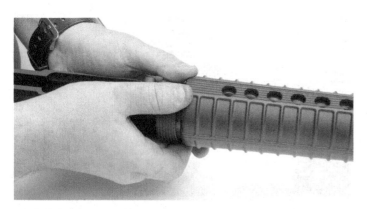

23) Turn over and repeat for the lower half of the hand-guard assembly.

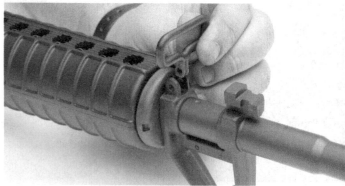

24) Position the sling swivel into place as shown.

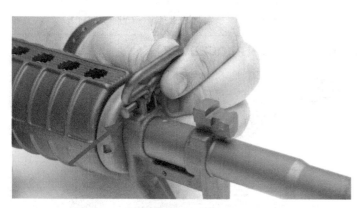

25) Install the sling rivet through the swivel to secure the swivel to the sight block frame.

26) Position the assembly into the rivet tool (rivet head toward the anvil side and rivet flange end toward the hammer side) and tap until the rivet is fully flared and secure in the sight post frame.

27) The sling rivet correctly installed.

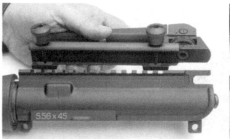

28) The A3 flat top upper receiver will accept the detachable carry handle/rear sight assembly. To install, simply fit the assembly onto the upper receiver's Picatinny rail, then tighten the carry handle retaining bolts finger tight to complete the installation.

Upper Receiver Assembly Parts
Installing the A2 Flash Hider

Parts needed:
  A2 flash hider
  Crush washer

Tools needed:
  Upper receiver vise clamps or barrel vise clamps
  Open-end wrench, 3/4"

A2 flash hider and crush washer.

1) Place the crush washer on the threaded muzzle (top). Being careful not to cross-thread, screw on the flash hider bottom).

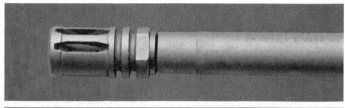

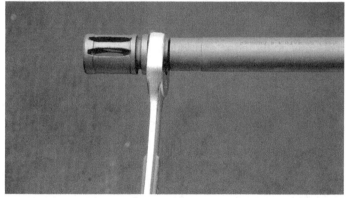

2) Once the flash hider is on the muzzle hand-tight (top), finish tightening it down using the 3/4" open-end wrench until the flash hider is correctly aligned (bottom).

3) Shown is the correct orientation of the flash hider: 12 o'clock position and solid on the bottom.

Upper Receiver Assembly Parts
Installing the Surefire Suppressor Adapter

Parts needed:
    Surefire suppressor adapter
    Spacers are included with the adapter.

Tools needed:
    Upper receiver vise clamps or barrel vise clamps
    Open-end wrench, ¾"

The Surefire suppressor adapter.

1) Screw on the adapter and fit it with shims for orientation.

2) Note that the SF logo is at the 2 o'clock position so when tightened down it will be at 12 o'clock.

3) Test-fit the adapter with the shims in place without Rockset on the threads.

4) Unscrew the adapter and cover the threads with the supplied Rockset.

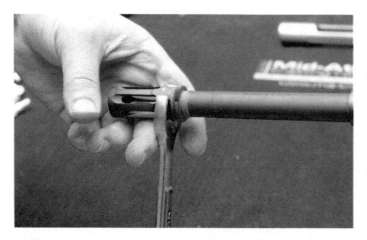

5) Tighten down the adapter and orient the SF logo at the top (12 o'clock).

6) The adapter is correctly oriented with the SF logo on the top (12 o'clock).

Upper Receiver Assembly Parts

Completing the Assembly of the Upper Receiver

Parts needed:
 Bolt carrier group
 Charging handle
 Upper receiver assembly

NOTE: Take the upper assembly out of the barrel vise.

NOTE: Shown is the installation of a PRI Gasbuster charging handle. All charging handles, including the MIL-SPEC version, install the same.

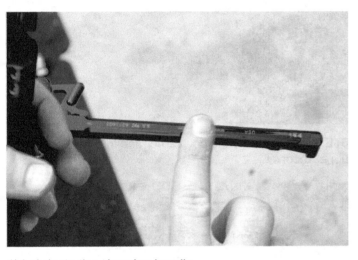

1) Lubricate the charging handle.

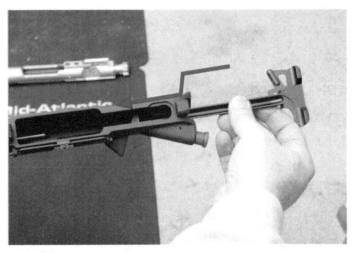

2) Correctly insert the charging handle into the receiver. Stop once it is half-way down.

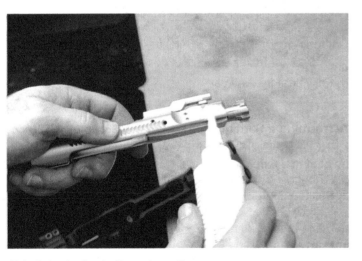

3) Lubricate the bolt carrier rails.

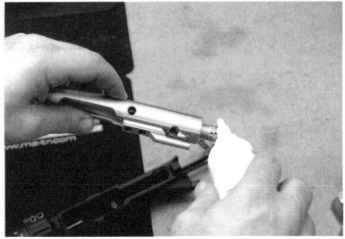

4) Lubricate the bolt lugs.

Upper Receiver Assembly Parts

**Completing the Assembly of the
  Upper Receiver**

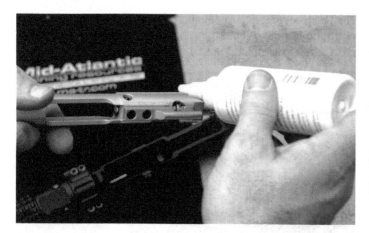

5) Lubricate the cam pin and cam pin hole.

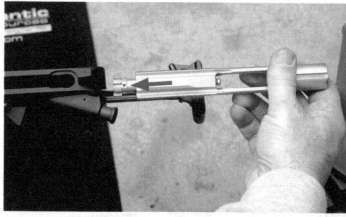

6) Extend the bolt in the bolt carrier and insert it into the upper receiver.

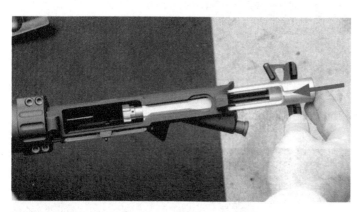

7) Slide the bolt carrier forward.

8) Fully seat the bolt carrier.

Performing a Function Check on the Completed Rifle

RENDER THE RIFLE SAFE (clear of ammunition and pointed in a safe direction)
1. Place the weapon on FIRE.
2. Pull the charging handle to the rear and release, allowing the bolt to go forward and lock into battery.
3. Place the weapon on SAFE.
4. Pull the trigger; nothing should happen.
5. Place the weapon on FIRE.
6. Pull the trigger and the hammer should release; continue to hold the trigger back.
7. Pull the charging handle to the rear and release; let up on the trigger and hear and feel the reset, then press the trigger to release the hammer.
8. Pull the charging handle to the rear and return it to its forward position.
9. Place the weapon on SAFE.

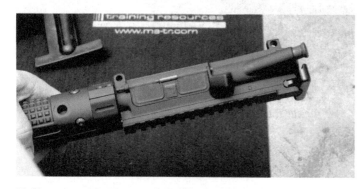

9) The completed upper receiver assembly.

SECTION 3
Using and Servicing the AR-15

WARNING: IT IS YOUR RESPONSIBILITY TO ENSURE THAT YOUR FIREARM IS HANDLED, FIRED, AND STORED SAFELY AND RESPONSIBLY AT ALL TIMES.

This manual provides instructions on the operation and maintenance of your AR-15 rifle. Read and understand it carefully before you try to use your firearm. Your safety, and that of those around you, depends on your knowledge of your firearm and your knowledge of safety rules common to all firearms. Please study the common-sense safety rules noted in this manual.

Your first responsibility as a gun owner is always safety!

Your second responsibility as a gun owner is security. Make sure that your firearm remains in responsible hands at all times! Don't become an unwitting partner in a crime or tragedy; make sure your firearm is properly secured. Lock it in a secure storage container or, if none is available, remove the bolt and bolt carrier assembly and store it separately. If you have more than one similar firearm, make sure that you specifically identify the removed assembly with its original firearm, because the assemblies may not be interchangeable.

It is also your responsibility to ensure that you comply with all federal, state, and local laws with regard to the purchase, ownership, use, and storage of your firearm.

NOTICE
VSS has no control over the use of your firearm, and shall not be responsible for injury, death, or damage to property resulting from either intentional or accidental discharge of this firearm. In addition, VSS shall not be responsible for proper function of the firearm when it is used for purposes or subjected to treatment for which it was not intended.

SAFETY FIRST...IT'S YOUR RESPONSIBILITY!

- Treat every gun as if it is loaded...AT ALL TIMES!

- Always keep the muzzle pointed in a safe direction.

- Never point your firearm at anything that you do not intend to destroy.

- Keep your finger off the trigger and out of the trigger guard until you are aiming at your target and are ready to shoot.

- Always keep the safety in the "SAFE" position, especially when the firearm is loaded and cocked, until you are ready to fire.

- Always keep and carry your firearm with an empty chamber until you intend to shoot so that your firearm cannot be fired unintentionally. Firearms should be unloaded when not actually in use.

- Be sure of your target and backstop before you shoot. Ask yourself what your bullet will hit if it misses or goes through the target.

- Never shoot at hard, flat surfaces or water...bullets can ricochet.

- Always wear hearing and eye protection when shooting.

- Discharging firearms in poorly ventilated areas, cleaning firearms, or handling ammunition may result in exposure to lead, a substance known to be associated with birth defects, reproductive harm, and other serious injury. Have adequate ventilation at all times and wash hands after handling.

- Be sure that your barrel is clear of obstructions, including excessive oil, grease, cleaning patches, et cetera before shooting.

- Use only clean, high-quality factory loaded ammunition in good condition.

- Do not alter or modify your firearm.

- Do not try to change your firearm's trigger pull; alterations of trigger pull can affect sear engagement and might cause accidental firing.

- Store firearms and ammunition separately and beyond children's reach.

IN CASE OF A MALFUNCTION, STOP! REVIEW THIS MANUAL TO IDENTIFY AND RESOLVE THE PROBLEM. IF YOU CANNOT RESOLVE IT, CONTACT THE MANUFACTURER OR A QUALIFIED GUNSMITH.

Using and Servicing the AR-15

Component Identification

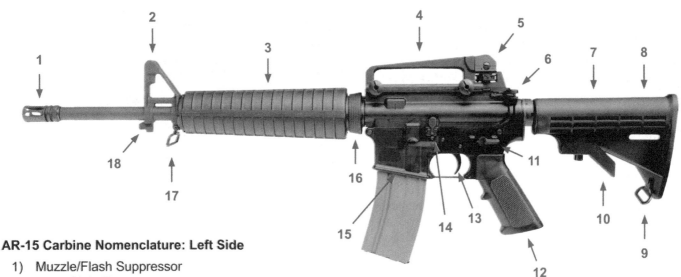

AR-15 Carbine Nomenclature: Left Side

1) Muzzle/Flash Suppressor
2) Front Sight Tower
3) Handguard
4) Carrying Handle
5) Rear Sight
6) Charging Handle
7) Buffer Extension Tube (under stock)
8) Buttstock
9) Rear Sling Attachment
10) Stock Adjustment Lever
11) Safety
12) Pistol Grip
13) Trigger
14) Bolt Release
15) Magazine Well
16) Slip Ring
17) Front Sling Attachment
18) Bayonet Lug
19) Magazine

AR-15 Carbine Nomenclature: Right Side

19) Magazine Release

Using and Servicing the AR-15

Clearing the AR-15

1) Ensure the rifle is on SAFE. At all time during the clearing you must never touch the trigger and must keep the muzzle pointed in a safe direction. If the safety selector will not rotate to SAFE, the hammer may be in the uncocked position. Pull the charging handle to the rear and release. Reattempt to place rifle on SAFE.

2) Remove the magazine by pressing in the magazine catch on the right side of the receiver/magazine well and pull the magazine downward from the weapon to release it. Place the magazine down or in a pouch.

3) Extract the cartridge (if any) from the chamber. To lock the bolt open, pull the charging handle rearward, press the bottom of the bolt catch, and allow the bolt to move forward until the bolt catch stops it. Return the charging handle forward. Observe the round extracting and ejecting from the ejection port; do not attempt to retain the round.

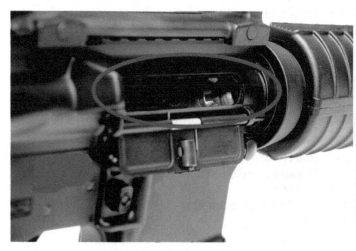

4) Visually observe that there is no magazine in the rifle and no round in the chamber. Physically check with your finger or use a flashlight in low-light conditions as needed.

NOTE: You must not reverse the steps listed above. If you clear and inspect the chamber prior to removing the magazine, you will load another round into the chamber when you release the charging handle. Always check the safety position and remove the magazine prior to clearing the chamber.

Using and Servicing the AR-15

Disassembling the AR-15

To ensure the proper function of the AR-15, it is necessary to disassemble the weapon to inspect and clean the internal components. The names of the parts should be learned through practice in disassembling and reassembling to enhance operator competence. Generally, the parts are named for the functions they perform (i.e. the trigger guard guards the trigger, the charging handle is used to charge the weapon, etc.). We have broken down the disassembly into normal operator field strip and detailed armor disassembly. Stay within your ability level or seek help from a knowledgable friend who can put your rifle back together.

Major components of M16/AR-15/M4 rifles:
1) Lower receiver and buttstock assembly
2) Upper receiver and barrel assembly
3) Charging Handle
4) Bolt and bolt carrier assembly

When the operator begins to disassemble the weapon, it should be done in the following order:

Upper and Lower Receivers

1) First, clear the weapon as previously described. Place the weapon on a flat, clean surface with the muzzle oriented in a safe direction. If necessary, remove the sling. Separate the upper and lower receivers by grasping the weapon by the buttstock and, with your free hand, push the take-down pin as far as it will go to the right. Do not force it. Next, pull the pin from the right side until it stops.

2) Push in the pivot pin as far as it will go to the right. Do not force it. Next, pull the pin from the right side until it stops. Lay the separated receivers down.

Using and Servicing the AR-15

Disassembling the AR-15

Charging handle and bolt carrier assembly

3) Unlock and pull back the charging handle and bolt carrier assembly. The charging handle release lever is not visible from this angle.

4) Lift the bolt carrier assembly off the charging handle.

5) Pull back and lift the charging handle so it will clear the upper receiver track.

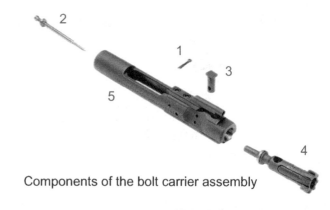

Components of the bolt carrier assembly

1. Firing Pin Retaining Pin; 2. Firing Pin; 3. Bolt Cam Pin;
4. Bolt Assembly; 5. Bolt Carrier

6) Move the bolt forward to the unlocked position and remove the firing pin retaining pin. The Glock punch tool works great for this. Do not open or close the split end of the firing pin retaining pin.

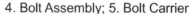

7) Push in on the bolt to put it in the rearward locked position.

Using and Servicing the AR-15

Disassembling the AR-15

Charging handle and bolt carrier assembly

8) Catch the firing pin as it drops out of the rear of the bolt carrier assembly.

9) Give the bolt cam pin a quarter-turn and lift it out.

10) Remove the bolt by pulling it from the front of the bolt carrier.

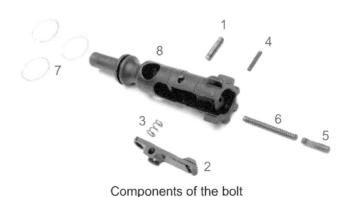

Components of the bolt

1. Extractor Pin; 2. Extractor; 3. Extractor Spring; 4. Ejector Pin; 5. Ejector; 6. Ejector Spring; 7. Gas Rings (3); 8. Bolt

11) Check the spring tension on the extractor by pressing on the rear of it. The extractor claw should return once released. If you are to disassemble the extractor, see steps 10 and 11. Replace the spring if it is found to be faulty.

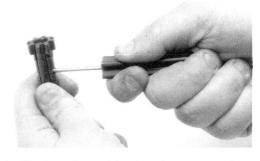

12) With a punch, Glock tool, cartridge head, or appropriate tool, remove the extractor pin.

Using and Servicing the AR-15

Disassembling the AR-15

Charging handle and bolt carrier assembly

Lower Receiver

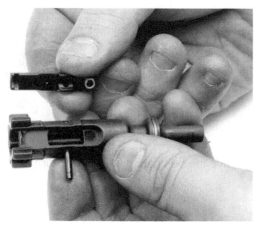

13) Remove the extractor and spring assembly. Do not remove the spring assembly, its insert, or the O-ring from the extractor unless you are upgrading this to a black buffer, five-coil spring and O-ring to enhance the extraction capability.

14) To remove the buffer, the hammer must be in the cocked position. Cock the hammer with your thumb, if needed. Push in the buffer and depress the retainer to release the buffer.

15) Remove the buffer. The buffer is under tension, so retain positive control of the buffer as you are removing it from the buffer tube.

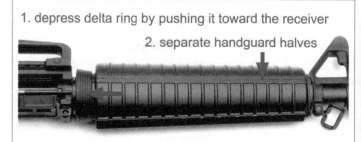

1. depress delta ring by pushing it toward the receiver

2. separate handguard halves

If you find it necessary to remove the handguard, it can be removed by depressing the delta ring and lifting out the separate halves of the handguard.

Using and Servicing the AR-15

Cleaning and Lubrication

The AR-15 is a dependable rifle, but routine cleaning is advised to ensure functionality. Clean the firearm as often as the situation dictates and the environment necessitates. Clean your rifle, keep it serviceable and know how it operates to make effective use of your time.

Keep the firearm free of dirt and dust as much as possible; use a muzzle cap or tape to keep them from the bore. Depending on the operating environment, keep lubricant only on metal-to-metal moving parts and use paintbrushes to clean dust and dirt off of and out of the firearm.

In hot and humid climates, frequently inspect the firearm for signs of rust. Keep the firearm free of moisture, and keep a fine coat of lubricating oil on the metal surfaces. If the firearm is exposed to salt air, high humidity, or water, then thoroughly clean and oil the firearm as often as needed to keep it serviceable.

In hot and dry climates, such as deserts, keep the firearm lubricated only on metal-to-metal moving parts, and use paint brushes to clean dust and dirt off of and out of the firearm. Keeping the firearm free of unneeded oil will prevent sand and dust from collecting in the receiver and bore.

Keep your ammunition in containers when not in use, and clean off the cartridges as necessary.

Clean the barrel with a cleaning rod or bore snake. Use solvent-saturated brass brushes to break up carbon in the bore, then use a solvent-covered patch to push out the carbon, followed by a dry patch until it is clean. A bore snake is a great bore-cleaning product to do this with, as the barrel is cleaned with one pass of the bore snake.

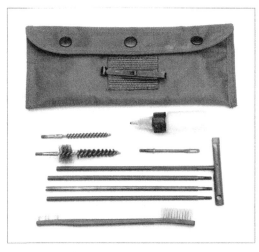

Standard cleaning kit

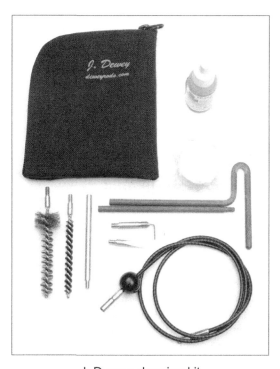

J. Dewey cleaning kit

Every AR-15 owner should have a quality cleaning kit with the appropriate brushes, jags, patches and lubricant. Some prefer the standard M4-type kits (left), but the J. Dewey kit (right) has proven to be a popular alternative due to its pull-through cable (which better protects the bore during cleaning versus the standard steel rods) and its compact design.

Using and Servicing the AR-15
Cleaning and Lubrication

Upper Receiver Assembly Cleaning

IMPORTANT! READ FIRST! ➡️

> **BARREL CLEANING TIPS:**
>
> • Clean the bore from the chamber to muzzle direction.
>
> • Do not reverse the direction of the bore brush while it is still in the bore (prevents ruining your brush). Push it completely out, then pull back through.
>
> • Use cleaning solvent on the bore and chamber, the gas tube, the upper receiver and barrel assembly, locking lugs, and all areas of powder fouling, corrosion, dirt, or dust.

1) Use a cleaning rod, bore brush, and cleaning solvent to break up initial carbon build-up in the bore. Run the brush through the chamber and flash suppressor several times. Next, assemble the rod and chamber brush for chamber cleaning and break up the carbon in the chamber and lug recesses. Apply cleaning solvent and insert the brush into the chamber and lug recesses. Clean by pushing and twisting the cleaning rod.

2) Use the multi-purpose brush or bore brush to clean the outside surface of the protruding gas tube. Do not use a serviceable bore brush to do this. Do not clean the inside of the gas tube.

Bolt Carrier Assembly and Charging Handle Cleaning

3 Once the bore and chamber have been brushed, replace the bore brush (shown) with the patch jag and use the cotton patches to remove the fouling from the bore and chamber area. Change patches until the bore and chamber are no longer fouled. As with the bore brush, do not change direction until the patch and jag are out of the muzzle. You may have to let the solvent sit on heavily built-up carbon deposits. Scraping may be required for built-up carbon.

4) Clean all parts and surfaces with a GI general-purpose brush/toothbrush, rag and/or swab saturated in powder cleaning solvent. Clean the bolt carrier key with a worn bore brush saturated with solvent, then dry with a pipe cleaner.

Using and Servicing the AR-15

Cleaning and Lubrication

Bolt Carrier Assembly and Charging Handle Cleaning

locking lugs

5) Remove carbon deposits from the locking lugs with a general purpose or worn bore brush saturated with solvent.

6) Clean the area behind the bolt rings. Carbon easily builds up in this area.

7) Clean under the lip of the extractor and check sharpness. Remove all brass shavings. If you did not remove the extractor from the bolt, press the ejector in repeatedly to remove accumulated brass shavings from the ejector hole and ensure the ejector moves freely. Lubricate it generously. If the spring does not have a noticeable amount of spring tension, replace the extractor and spring.

8) Clean the carbon from the outside surfaces of the charging handle.

Lower Receiver Assembly Cleaning

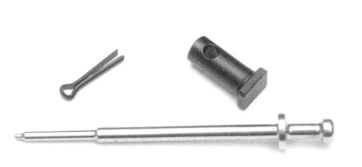

9) Clean the firing pin, retaining pin, and cam pin.

- Wipe and/or brush dirt and sand from the trigger and trigger guard.

- Wipe and/or brush powder fouling, corrosion, and foreign matter from the lower receiver assembly.

- Wipe the lower receiver, buffer, and buffer spring with a solvent-soaked rag.

- Use a dry rag or pressurized air to dry the parts.

Using and Servicing the AR-15
Cleaning and Lubrication

Upper Receiver Assembly Lubrication

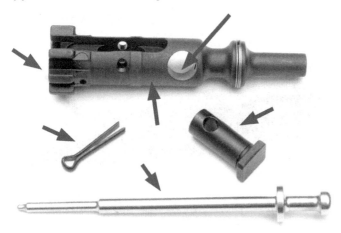

Lubricate the outside of the bolt cam pin and the firing pin retaining pin. Make certain to lubricate the bolt cam pin hole, bolt gas rings, and outside of the bolt. Excess lube will be blown out with the first shot, so there is no need to over-lubricate.

Lightly lubricate the inner and outer surfaces of the bolt carrier. Generously lubricate the slide and cam pin area of the bolt carrier. Dry the bolt carrier key tube with a pipe cleaner. **Note:** DO NOT excessively attempt to scrap the carbon deposits on the inside of the carrier as you can damage it.

Completing the Lubrication

• Lightly lubricate the charging handle.

• Lightly lubricate the recoil spring and buffer.

• Lubricate take-down pins and the inside parts (only where metal moves on metal) of the lower receiver.

• Lightly lubricate the bore and chamber with a lightly lubricated patch on the cleaning rod.

• Lubricate the locking lugs.

• Apply a drop of lubricant onto the front sight detent and depress to ensure it works properly.

IMPORTANT CLEANING TIPS:

• Do not use wire-type brushes or abrasive material to clean aluminum surfaces.

• Do not use any abrasive cleaners or wire brushes on the upper or lower receivers.

IMPORTANT LUBRICATION TIP:

• Do not use any lubricant containing graphite. Graphite can cause corrosion in aluminum alloys.

GENERAL CLEANING/LUBRICATION INFORMATION

Firearm-specific cleaners and lubricants are best to use; however, spray carburetor cleaner (in well-ventilated areas) is useful for removing carbon build-up in the upper receiver and bolt carrier assemblies. In areas where firearm-specific cleaners and lubricants cannot be obtained, testing by Rock Island Arsenal has found that Automatic Transmission Fluid can be safely used as a cleaner and light lubricant. Also, 20-weight synthetic motor oil can be used as a lubricant with no harmful effects to the firearm.

Lubricate all operating parts. Inside the receiver, coat the metal in a light film of CLP or light machine gun oil. Some types of grease (like TW-25B) can be used on the metal-to-metal (shiny spot) areas to allow the rifle to operate smoothly.

FIREARM PROTECTION

Use a type of Cleaner/Lubricant/Protectant (CLP). When not available, some prefer motor oil, automatic transmission fluid, or light gun oil. With a rag, wipe down all exposed metal with CLP, interior and exterior, parkerized, blued, or otherwise. A slight film is all that is required to protect the firearm.

Using and Servicing the AR-15
Assembling the AR-15

Lower Receiver Assembly

Bolt Carrier Assembly and Charging Handle

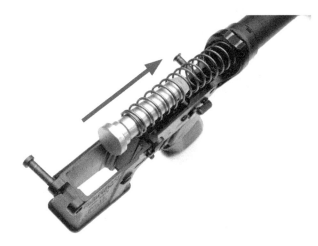

1) Insert the buffer and buffer spring into the buffer tube and push past the buffer retaining pin by depressing it downward.

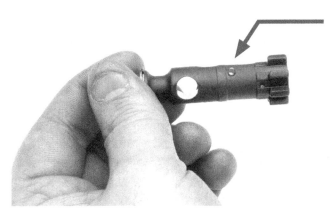

2) If the extractor spring separates from the extractor, reinsert the large end of the extractor spring in the extractor. Ensure the reinforcement ring is around the spring. Insert the extractor with the spring assembly into the bolt. Push the extractor until the holes on the extractor and bolt are aligned, then insert the extractor pin.

3) Staggering gas rings on the bolt does nothing to help prevent the loss of any gas. When inserted into the carrier, they are compressed flush. (Photo simulated to show ring compression in the bolt carrier.)

4) Slide the bolt assembly into the bolt carrier far enough to insert the cam pin. Ensure you have the bolt with the extractor on the right side so the cam pin hole will line up for the cam pin insertion. Insert the bolt cam pin and give it a quarter-turn.

5) Insert the firing pin into the rear of the bolt.

6) Pull the bolt assembly forward and insert the firing pin retaining pin in the area between the large flange and the blunt end of the firing pin.

Using and Servicing the AR-15
Assembling the AR-15

Bolt Carrier Assembly and Charging Handle

7) Turn the bolt carrier assembly up and attempt to shake out the firing pin (right). The firing pin must not fall out. If the firing pin does fall out, remove the firing pin retaining pin, fully reinsert the firing pin, and reinsert the firing pin retaining pin. Recheck for proper assembly. The rifle will not fire if the retaining pin is not properly securing the firing pin.

8) Place the charging handle into the upper receiver and engage the handle's lugs with the track in the receiver, then push the charging handle part-way into the upper receiver.

9) With the bolt extended, slide the bolt carrier assembly into the upper receiver.

10) Push the charging handle assembly and bolt carrier assembly together into the upper receiver.

11) Align the upper and lower receivers. Align the pivot pin holes with the pivot pin and push the front pivot pin in. Note the hammer must be in the cocked position; press it down with your thumb to cock.

12) Close the upper and lower receivers. Push in the rear take-down pin.

Using and Servicing the AR-15

Assembling the AR-15

Handguard and Sling

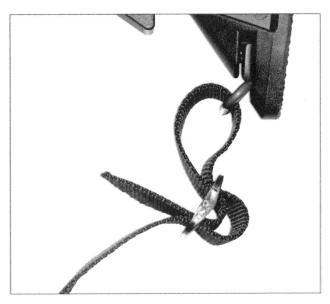

14) Reattach your sling if you removed it prior to disassembly.

13) If you have removed your handguards, use a buddy system or grow a third arm to fight them back on. To reinstall the hand guard:

A. Place the weapon on its buttstock, with one hand gripping the stock. Insert one handguard into the handguard cap at the top.

B. Press down or use a handguard tool to press down on the slip ring and install one half of the handguard under the slip ring.

C. Repeat these steps to install the second half of the handguard.

SAFETY AND FUNCTION CHECK!

1. Ensure the firearm is clear of all ammunition and pointed in a safe direction.

2. Pull the charging handle to the rear and release it. Place the selector on SAFE. Squeeze the trigger and the hammer should not fall.

3. Place the selector on FIRE. Squeeze the trigger and hold the trigger to the rear. The hammer should fall. While holding the trigger to the rear, pull the charging handle to the rear and release it. You should hear a click as you release the trigger. Squeeze the trigger again; the hammer should fall.

4. Pull the charging handle to the rear again. Release, then place the firearm on SAFE.

NOTE: If your rifle fails any of these tests, check your assembly. If the rifle will not pass these checks and it has been assembled properly, contact a qualified gunsmith for assistance.

Using and Servicing the AR-15

Servicing the M16/M4 Magazine

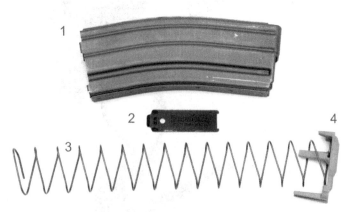

Magazine Components: 1. magazine body; 2. magazine floor plate; 3. spring; 4. follower

1) To disassemble the magazine, ensure the magazine is unloaded, with no ammo. Use a bullet or pointed object to depress the retaining plate through the floor plate and start to slide the floor plate to the rear. The older, dirtier, and/or rustier the magazine is the harder this step will be to do. Be careful not to slide the floor plate fully off until you are ready to apply pressure to the retainer plate, as it is under spring tension.

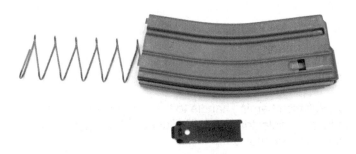

2) Once you have the floor plate started, use your thumb to hold the retainer plate and fully remove the floor plate. Now you can release the spring tension in a controlled manner and remove the spring and follower from the magazine body. The follower and retaining plate can be removed from the spring if needed for thorough cleaning.

3) The fully disassembled magazine.

It is important to clean the inside of the magazine body and the outside of the follower. Keep the magazine as dry as possible, but lightly coated with a protectant to prevent rusting.

To reassemble, just reverse the process.

Using and Servicing the AR-15
Loading the 20- or 30-Round Magazine

MAGAZINE-LOADING TIP
The magazine can hold 30 cartridges, but due to the possibility of having to load with the bolt carrier forward, we prefer to load 29 rounds in the first magazine, then load the chamber so you have 28 in the magazine and one in the chamber. Then load 28-rounds in the magazines placed in your pouches (just personal preference). It is easiest to lay out the number of rounds for each magazine so you don't have to count the rounds as you load the magazine, or just strip two off a stripper clip in the set of three.

IMPORTANT!
Ensure the magazines are clean, rust-free, and without damage. Observe basic safety precautions of handling small arms ammunition at all times.

Ensure you have 5.56x45mm ammunition. This ammunition is easily confused with 5.45 x 39mm (AK74). Inspect it for uniformity, cleanliness, and serviceability. Check all cartridges for undented primers, and only use issued ammunition.

1) Use your non-dominant hand to hold the magazine as shown.

2) With your dominant hand, one at a time, place the cartridge over the top of the magazine follower between the feed lips and press the cartridge straight down until it snaps under the feed lips.

3) Once the cartridge is under the lip of the magazine body, slide it fully to the rear so the next round will be able to be pushed down.

Using and Servicing the AR-15
Loading the AR-15

Loading from the Open Bolt

1) Lock the bolt carrier to the rear by pulling the charging handle fully to the rear. Press and hold the bottom of the bolt lock lever. Release the tension on the charging handle and return it to its forward locked position. Place the safety, located on the left-hand side of the firearm, to the (SAFE) position. **NOTE:** The firearm will not go onto SAFE if the hammer is not cocked.

2) Insert the top of the magazine into the magazine well (bullets towards the end of the muzzle) and press the magazine upwards to lock it in.

3) Ensure that the magazine is locked into place by slightly tugging down on it. Do not abuse your magazines by loading 30 rounds and slamming it into a rifle with the bolt forward.

4) Depress the upper portion of the bolt catch to release the bolt. Tap the forward assist and close the dust cover. Checking the magazine to ensure chambering can be done by removing the magazine and looking to see if the round on top is on the opposite side from when first inserted prior to chambering, and/or unlock and observe by slightly retracting the charging handle until you see or feel the brass of the cartridge. Release the charging handle and once again tap the forward assist to ensure the bolt is in battery.

Using and Servicing the AR-15

Loading the AR-15

Loading from the Closed Bolt

1) Insert the magazine until the magazine catch engages.

2) Pull down slightly to ensure proper lock up. NEVER force or pound the magazine into the receiver. Fully loaded magazines may not lock into the magazine catch; one round should be removed to allow for easier lock up.

3) Fully pull back on the charging handle and release with your non-dominant hand. As the bolt travels forward by the firearm's spring tension it will strip the top round from the magazine and force it into the chamber. It is a good habit to tap the forward assist to ensure the bolt is fully forward and in battery. Riding the charging handle forward will not allow for the bolt to fully return to battery.

4) If you are preparing the rifle to fire, it is now ready; otherwise, ensure the selector is in the safe position. Keep the safety on SAFE until you intend to shoot.

Press-Check Procedure

5) To check if the chamber was loaded with a round, with the safety still engaged, pull the charging handle back slightly to see the cartridge being pulled from the chamber.

6) Once you have seen or felt the cartridge in the chamber, return the charging handle forward and tap the forward assist to ensure the bolt is in battery. In low-light conditions, you may have to reach in and feel the cartridge casing to determine if the chamber is loaded.

Using and Servicing the AR-15
Firing the AR-15: Basic Rifle Fundamentals

INTRODUCTION
The shooter must understand and apply the four key fundamentals before he approaches the firing line. He must establish a steady position, allowing observation of the target. He must aim the rifle at the target by aligning the sight system, and fire the rifle without disturbing this alignment by improper breathing or during the trigger squeeze. These skills are known collectively as the four fundamentals. Applying these four fundamentals rapidly and consistently is the integrated act of firing.

> **OVERVIEW**
> Orient toward the desired area/target, take a proper sight alignment and sight picture, rotate the selector/ safety lever 90° to the FIRE position and press the trigger straight to the rear without interrupting your sight alignment and sight picture.
>
> Once your target engagement is complete, rotate the selector to the rear SAFE position (up).

I. Steady Position

When the shooter approaches the firing line, he should assume a comfortable, steady firing position. He should learn how to establish a steady position during the integrated act of dry-fire training. Dry firing is the practice of "firing" a firearm without ammunition. That is, to pull the trigger and allow the hammer or striker to drop on an empty chamber. The shooter is the best judge of the quality of his position. If he can hold the front sight post steady through the fall of the hammer, he has a good position.

The steady position elements are:

(1) Non-firing Handgrip. The rifle hand guard rests on the heel of the hand in the V formed by the thumb and fingers. The grip of the non-firing hand is light.

(2) Rifle Butt Position. The butt of the rifle is placed in the pocket of the firing shoulder. This reduces the effect of recoil and helps maintain a steady position.

(3) Firing Handgrip. The firing hand grasps the pistol grip so it fits the V formed by the thumb and forefinger. The forefinger is placed on the trigger so the lay of the rifle is not disturbed when the trigger is squeezed. A slight rear-

ward pressure is exerted by the remaining three fingers to ensure that the butt of the stock remains in the pocket of the shoulder, minimizing the effect of recoil.

(4) Firing Elbow Placement. The firing elbow is important in providing balance. Its exact location depends on the firing position used. Placement should allow the shoulders to remain level.

(5) Non-firing Elbow. The non-firing elbow is positioned firmly under the rifle to allow a comfortable and stable position. When the shooter engages a wide sector of fire, moving targets, and targets at various elevations, his non-firing elbow should remain free from support.

(6) Cheek-to-Stock Weld. The stock weld should provide a natural line of sight through the center of the rear sight aperture to the front sight post and on to the target. The shooter's neck should be relaxed, allowing his cheek to fall naturally onto the stock. Through dry-fire training, the shooter practices this position until he assumes the same cheek-to-stock weld each time he assumes a given position, which provides consistency in aiming. Proper eye relief is obtained when a shooter establishes a good cheek-to-stock weld. A small change in eye relief normally occurs each time that the shooter assumes a different firing

Using and Servicing the AR-15
Firing the AR-15: Basic Rifle Fundamentals

I. Steady Position (continued)

position. The shooter should begin by trying to touch the charging handle with his nose when assuming a firing position. This will aid the shooter in maintaining the same cheek-to-stock weld hold each time the weapon is aimed. The shooter should be mindful of how the nose touches the charging handle, and should be consistent when doing so. This should be critiqued and reinforced during dry-fire training.

(7) Support. When artificial support (sandbags, logs, stumps) is available, it should be used to steady the position and support the rifle. If it is not available, then the bones, not the muscles, in the shooter's upper body must support the rifle.

(8) Muscle Relaxation. If support is used properly, the shooter should be able to relax most of his muscles. Using artificial support or bones in the upper body as support allows him to relax and settle into position. Using muscles to support the rifle can cause the rifle to move due to muscle fatigue.

(9) Natural Point of Aim. When the shooter first assumes his firing position, he orients his rifle in the general direction of his target. Then he adjusts his body to bring the rifle and sights exactly in line with the desired aiming point. When using proper support and consistent cheek-to-stock weld, the shooter should have his rifle and sights aligned naturally on the target. When correct body-rifle-target alignment is achieved, the front sight post must be held on target, using muscular support and effort. As the rifle fires, muscles tend to relax, causing the front sight to move away from the target toward the natural point of aim. Adjusting this point to the desired point of aim eliminates this movement. When multiple target exposures are expected (or a sector of fire must be covered), the shooter adjusts his natural point of aim to the center of the expected target exposure area (or center of sector).

II. Aiming

Having mastered the task of holding the rifle steady, the shooter must align the rifle with the target in exactly the same way for each firing. The shooter is the final judge as to where his eye is focused. The instructor or trainer emphasizes this point by having the shooter focus on the target and then focus back on the front sight post. He checks

Correct sight alignment

the position of the firing eye to ensure it is in line with the rear sight aperture.

(1) Rifle Sight Alignment. Alignment of the rifle with the target is critical. It involves placing the tip of the front sight post in the center of the rear sight aperture (above). Any alignment error between the front and rear sights repeats itself for every 1/2 meter the bullet travels. For example, at the 25-meter line, any error in rifle alignment is multiplied 50 times. If the bullet is misaligned by 1/10 inch, it causes a target at 300 meters to be missed by 5 feet.

(2) Focus of the Eye. A proper firing position places the eye directly in line with the center of the rear sight aperture. When the eye is focused on the front sight post, the natural ability of the eye to center objects in a circle and to seek the point of greatest light (center of the aperture) aid in providing correct sight alignment. For the average shooter firing at combat-type targets, the natural ability of the eye can accurately align the sights. Therefore, the shooter can place the tip of the front sight post on the aiming point, but the eye must be focused on the tip of the front sight post. This causes the target to appear blurry, while the front sight post is seen clearly. Two reasons for focusing on the front sight post are:

(a) Only a minor aiming error should occur since the error reflects only as much as the shooter fails to determine the target center. A greater aiming error can result if the front sight post is blurry due to focusing on the target or other objects.

Using and Servicing the AR-15
Firing the AR-15: Basic Rifle Fundamentals

II. Aiming (continued)

(b) Focusing on the tip of the front sight post aids the shooter in maintaining proper sight alignment (see next illustration).

(3) Sight Picture. Once the shooter can correctly align his sights, he can obtain a sight picture. A correct sight picture has the target, front sight post, and rear sight aligned. The sight picture includes two basic elements: sight alignment and placement of the aiming point.

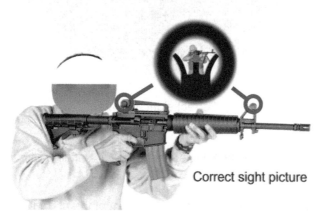
Correct sight picture

(a) Placement of the aiming point varies depending on the engagement range. For example, the above photo shows a silhouette at 300 meters where the aiming point is the center of mass, and the sights are aligned for a correct sight picture.

(b) A technique to obtain a good sight picture is the side aiming technique (above). It involves positioning the front sight post to the side of the target in line with the vertical center of mass, keeping the sights aligned. The front sight post is moved horizontally until the target is directly centered on the front sight post.

(4) Front Sight. The front sight post is vital to proper firing and should be replaced when damaged. The post should be blackened any time it is shiny, since precise focusing on the tip of the front sight post cannot be done otherwise.

(5) Aiming Practice. Aiming practice is conducted before firing live rounds. During day firing, the shooter should practice sight alignment and placement of the aiming point. Using training aids such as the M15A1 aiming card can do this.

III. Breath Control

As the shooter's skills improve and as timed or multiple targets are presented, he must learn to control his breath at any part of the breathing cycle. Two types of breath control techniques are practiced during dry fire. The coach/trainer ensures that the shooter uses two breathing techniques and understands them by instructing him to exaggerate his breathing. The shooter must be aware of the rifle's move-ment (while sighted on a target) as a result of breathing.

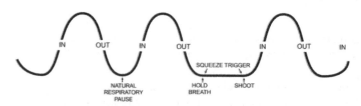

(1) Breath Control for Engaging Single Targets. The first technique is used during zeroing, and when time is avail-able to fire a shot (above). There is a moment of natural respiratory pause while breathing when most of the air has been exhaled from the lungs and before inhaling. Breathing should stop after most of the air has been exhaled during the normal breathing cycle. The shot must be fired before the shooter feels any discomfort.

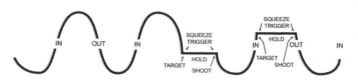

(2) Breath Control for Engaging Short-Exposure Targets. The second breath control technique is employed during rapid fire short-exposure targets (above). Using this technique, the shooter stops his breath when he is about to squeeze the trigger.

Using and Servicing the AR-15

Firing the AR-15: Basic Rifle Fundamentals

IV. Trigger Squeeze

A shooter can learn to place the rifle in a steady position and to correctly aim at the target if he follows the basic principles. Yet if the trigger is not properly squeezed, the rifle will be misaligned with the target at the moment of firing.

(1) Rifle Movement. Trigger squeeze is important for two reasons. First, any sudden movement of the finger on the trigger can disturb the lay of the rifle and cause the shot to miss the target. Second, the precise instant of firing should be a surprise to the shooter. The shooter's natural reflex to compensate for the noise and slight punch in the shoulder can cause him to miss the target if he knows the exact instant the rifle will fire. The soldier usually tenses his shoulders when expecting the rifle to fire. It is difficult to detect since he does not realize he is flinching. When the hammer drops on a dummy round and does not fire, the shooter's natural reflexes demonstrate that he is improperly squeezing the trigger.

(2) Trigger Finger. The trigger finger (index finger on the firing hand) is placed on the trigger between the first joint and the tip of the finger (not the extreme end) and adjusted depending on hand size, grip, and so on. The trigger finger must squeeze the trigger to the rear so the hammer falls without disturbing the lay of the rifle. When a live round is fired, it is difficult to see what effect trigger pull had on the lay of the rifle. It is important to experiment with many finger positions during dry-fire training to ensure the hammer is falling with little disturbance to the aiming process.

(a) As the shooter's skills increase with practice, he needs to spend less time on trigger squeeze. Novice shooters can take five seconds to perform an adequate trigger squeeze but, as skills improve, he can squeeze the trigger in a second or less. The proper trigger squeeze should start with slight pressure on the trigger during the initial aiming process. The shooter applies more pressure after the front sight post is steady on the target and he is holding his breath.

(b) The coach/trainer observes the trigger squeeze, emphasizes the correct procedure, and checks the shooter's applied pressure. He places his finger on the trigger and has the shooter squeeze the trigger by applying pressure to the coach/trainer's finger. The coach/trainer ensures that the shooter squeezes straight to the rear on the trigger, avoiding a left or right twisting movement. The coach/trainer observes that the shooter follows through and holds the trigger to the rear for approximately one second after the round has been fired. A steady position reduces disturbance of the rifle during trigger squeeze.

(c) Wobble area is the movement of the front sight around the aiming point when the rifle is in the steadiest position. From an unsupported position, the shooter experiences a greater wobble area than from a supported position. If the front sight strays from the target during the firing process, pressure on the trigger should be held constant and resumed as soon as sighting is corrected. The position must provide for the smallest possible wobble area. From a supported position, there should be minimal wobble area and little reason to detect movement. If movement of the rifle causes the front sight to leave the target, more practice is needed. The shooter should never try to quickly squeeze the trigger while the sight is on the target. The best firing performance results when the trigger is squeezed continuously, and the rifle is fired without disturbing its lay.

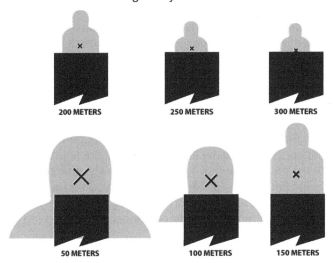

Aiming point for a 25-meter zero. "X" denotes the bullet strike point when the front sight is aligned on the target as illustrated.

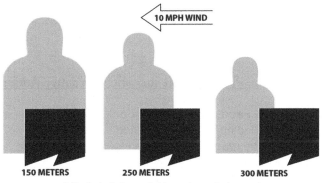

Adjusted aiming point based on wind speed.

Using and Servicing the AR-15

Malfunctions / Troubleshooting

A malfunction is a failure of the firearm to function properly. Defective ammunition or improper operation of the firearm by an operator is not considered a malfunction of the firearm. Malfunctions are caused by procedural or mechanical failures of the rifle, magazine, or ammunition. Pre-firing checks and serviceability inspections identify potential problems before they become malfunctions.

Malfunction and Immediate Action Procedures

Sluggish operation and the corrective action: Sluggish operation (gun cycles slowly) of the weapon is usually due to excessive friction caused by dirt or carbon, lack of proper lubrication, burred parts or excessive loss of gas. To correct this problem you must disassemble, clean, and lubricate the weapon while inspecting the parts for burrs or damage. Replace parts as necessary.

Stoppages: A stoppage is an interruption in the cycle of operation caused by a faulty gun or ammunition. In short, the gun stops firing. A stoppage must be cleared quickly by applying immediate action.

Immediate Action: This is the prompt action taken by the gunner to reduce a stoppage of the rifle without investigating the cause. If the gun stops firing, the shooter performs immediate action. Hang fire and cook off are two terms that describe ammunition condition and should be understood in conjunction with immediate-action procedures.

Hang Fire: Occurs when the cartridge primer has detonated after being struck by the firing pin, but some problem with the powder causes it to burn too slowly, and this delays the firing of the projectile. Time (5 seconds) is allotted for this malfunction before investigating a stoppage further because of potential injury to personnel and damage to equipment.

Cook Off: Occurs when the heat of the weapon is high enough to cause the propellant powder inside the round to ignite even though the primer has not been struck. Immediate action is to unload the weapon promptly and allow it to cool prior to reloading and firing.

Malfunctions, Probable Causes, and Corrective Actions

1. Failure to Feed, Chamber, or Lock. A malfunction can occur when loading the rifle, or during the cycle of operation. Once the magazine has been loaded into the rifle, the forward movement of the bolt carrier group could lack enough force (generated by the expansion of the action spring) to feed, chamber, or lock the bolt.

Probable Causes: The cause could be the result of one or more of the following–

• Excess accumulation of dirt or fouling in and around the bolt and bolt carrier.

• Defective magazine (dented, bulged, or a weak magazine spring).

• Improperly loaded magazine.

• Defective round (projectile forced back into the cartridge case, which could result in a stubbed round, or the base of the previous cartridge could have separated, leaving the remainder in the chamber).

• Damaged or broken action spring.

• Exterior accumulation of dirt in the lower receiver extension.

• Fouled gas tube resulting in short recoil.

• A magazine resting on the ground or pushed forward could cause an improper lock.

Corrective Action: Applying immediate action usually corrects the malfunction. To avoid the risk of further jamming, the shooter should watch for ejection of a cartridge and ensure that the upper receiver is free of any loose rounds. If immediate action fails to clear the malfunction, remedial action must be taken. The carrier should not be forced. If resistance is encountered, which can occur with an unserviceable round, the bolt should be locked to the rear, the magazine removed, and the malfunction cleared. For example, a bolt override is when a cartridge has wedged itself between the bolt and charging handle. The best way to correct this problem is by–

• Ensuring the charging handle is pushed forward and locked in place.

• Securing the rifle and pulling the bolt to the rear until the bolt seats completely into the buffer well.

• Turning the rifle upright and allowing the overridden cartridge to fall out.

2. Failure to Fire Cartridge. This is a failure of a cartridge to fire despite the fact that a round has been chambered, the trigger pulled, and the sear released the hammer. This occurs when the firing pin fails to strike the primer with enough force, or when the ammunition is defective.

Using and Servicing the AR-15

Malfunctions / Troubleshooting

Malfunctions, Probable Causes, and Corrective Actions

Immediate action: This action is performed when the operator has a failure to fire, which is when the trigger is pulled, the hammer moves forward, and the weapon does not fire.

    SPORTS, Failure to Fire

- **S**lap up on the bottom of the magazine
- **P**ull the charging handle to the rear
- **O**bserve the chamber for ejection of the round
- **R**elease the charging handle
- **T**ap the forward assist
- **S**queeze the trigger again

If, during your recharging of the action, you observe a cartridge case or a round that is not ejected, then perform remedial action.

Remedial Action: When immediate action fails to reduce the stoppage, remedial action must be taken. To do so tactically is to release the magazine, recharge the action 3-4 times, watching for the round to be extracted and ejected, reload the magazine into the firearm, charge the rifle, and attempt to refire. Administratively prior to investigating the cause of the stoppage, you must clear the firearm, and this step may involve some disassembly of the firearm and replacement of parts to correct the problem. Remedial actions for stoppages are as follows...

Probable Causes: Excessive carbon buildup on the firing pin is often the cause since the full forward travel of the firing pin is restricted. A defective or worn firing pin can give the same results. Inspection of the ammunition could reveal a shallow indentation or no mark on the primer, indicating a firing pin malfunction. Cartridges that show a normal indentation on the primer but fail to fire indicate faulty ammunition.

Corrective Action: If the malfunction continues, the firing pin, bolt, carrier, and locking lug recesses of the barrel extension should be inspected and any accumulation of excessive carbon or fouling should be removed. The firing pin should also be inspected for damage. Cartridges that show a normal indentation on the primer but fail to fire could indicate a bad ammunition lot. Those that show a complete penetration of the primer by the firing pin could also indicate failure of the cartridge to fully seat in the chamber.

WARNING: If an audible "POP" or reduced recoil occurs during firing, immediately cease-fire. This POP or reduced recoil could be the result of a round being fired without enough force to send the projectile out of the barrel. Do not apply immediate action. Remove the magazine, lock the bolt to the rear, and place the selector lever in the SAFE position. Visually inspect the bore to ensure a projectile is not lodged in the barrel. If a projectile is lodged in the barrel, do not try to remove it.

3. Failure to Extract. A failure to extract results when the cartridge case remains in the chamber of the rifle. This creates a serious stoppage/malfunction when the bolt and bolt carrier recoils fully to the rear and upon its return forward strips a live round out of the magazine and forces it into the case already stuck in the chamber. This malfunction is one of the hardest to clear.

WARNING: A failure to extract is considered an extremely serious malfunction, requiring the use of tools to clear. A live round could be left in the chamber and accidentally discharged. If a second live round is fed into the primer of the chambered live round, the rifle could explode and cause personal injury. This malfunction must be properly identified and reported. Failures to eject (see next page), should not be reported as extraction failures.

Probable Cause: Short recoil cycles and fouled or corroded rifle chambers are the most common causes of failures to extract. A damaged extractor or a weak or broken extractor spring can also cause this malfunction.

Corrective Action: The severity of a failure to extract determines the corrective action procedures. If the bolt has moved rearward far enough to strip a live round from the magazine in its forward motion, the bolt and carrier must be locked to the rear. The magazine and all loose rounds must be removed before clearing the stoppage. Tapping the butt of the rifle on a hard surface usually causes the cartridge to fall out of the chamber; however, if the cartridge case is ruptured, it may be lodged in the chamber. When this occurs, a cleaning rod can be inserted into the bore from the muzzle end. The cartridge case can be forced from the chamber by tapping the cleaning rod against the inside base of the fired cartridge. If cleaning and inspecting the mechanism and chamber reveals no defects but failures to extract persist, the extractor and extractor spring should be replaced. If the chamber surface is damaged, the entire barrel must be replaced.

Using and Servicing the AR-15
Malfunctions / Troubleshooting

Malfunctions, Probable Causes, and Corrective Actions

4. Failure to Eject. Ejection of a cartridge is an element in the cycle of functioning of the rifle, regardless of the mode of fire. A malfunction occurs when the cartridge is not ejected through the ejection port and either remains partly in the chamber or becomes jammed in the upper receiver as the bolt closes. When the shooter initially clears the rifle, the cartridge could strike an inside surface of the receiver and bounce back into the path of the bolt.

Probable Cause: The cartridge must extract before it can eject. Failures to eject can also be caused by a buildup of carbon or fouling on the ejector spring or extractor, or from short recoil. Short recoil is usually due to a buildup of fouling in the carrier mechanism or gas tube, which could result in many failures to include a failure to eject. Resistance caused by a carbon-coated or corroded chamber can impede the extraction, and the ejection of a cartridge.

Corrective Action: While retraction of the charging handle usually frees the cartridge and permits removal, the charging handle must not be released until the position of the next live round is determined. If another live round has been sufficiently stripped from the magazine or remains in the chamber, then the magazine and all live rounds could also require removal before the charging handle can be released. If several malfunctions occur and are not corrected by cleaning and lubricating, the ejector spring, extractor spring, and extractor should be replaced.

5. Other Malfunctions. The following paragraphs describe some other malfunctions that can occur.

1. **The bolt fails to remain in a rearward position after the last round in the magazine is fired.** Check for a bad magazine or short recoil.

2. **The bolt fails to lock in the rearward position when the bolt catch has been engaged.** Inspect the bolt catch and replace if necessary.

3. **The trigger fails to pull or return after release with the selector set in a firing position.** This indicates that the trigger pin has backed out of the receiver or the hammer spring is broken. Replace or repair.

4. **The magazine fails to lock into the magazine well.** Check the magazine and magazine catch for damage. Adjust the catch or replace as required.

5. **Any part of the bolt carrier group fails to function.** Check for incorrect assembly of components. Correctly clean and assemble the bolt carrier group, or replace the damaged parts.

6. **The ammunition fails to feed from the magazine.** Check for damaged magazine. A damaged magazine could cause repeated feeding failures and should be rendered unusable and discarded.

6. Misfire Procedures

Stuck Cartridge: Some swelling of the cartridge occurs when it fires. If the swelling is excessive, the cartridge will be fixed tightly in the chamber. If the extractor spring has weakened and does not tightly grip the base of the cartridge, it may fail to extract a round when the bolt moves to the rear. Clear the firearm prior to this corrective action.

Ensure the bolt is held to the rear and use the cleaning rod to punch down from the muzzle to dislodge the stuck casing. Prior to doing these actions, allow the weapon to cool if at all possible.

Ruptured Cartridge: Sometimes a cartridge is in a weakened condition after firing. In addition, it may swell as described above. In this case, a properly functioning extractor may sometimes tear the base of the cartridge off as the bolt moves to the rear, leaving the rest of the cartridge wedged inside the chamber. The ruptured cartridge extractor tool must be used in this instance to remove it. Clear the firearm. Disassemble the firearm by removing the bolt carrier. Insert the shell extractor tool, which is attached to the cleaning rod, into the chamber to grip and remove the remains of the cartridge. Inspect the bore and reassemble the firearm.

Using and Servicing the AR-15

Malfunctions / Troubleshooting

Problem	Check For	What To Do
Won't Fire	• Selector lever on SAFE	Put selector lever on FIRE
	• Improper assembly of firing pin	Assemble correctly
	• Oil or fouling in bolt	Clean with pipe cleaner
	• Defective ammunition	Replace with proper ammo
	• Excess carbon build-up on firing pin or in firing pin recess	Clean
Bolt Won't Lock	• Dirty bolt	Clean
	• Burred or broken bolt	Replace with new bolt
Failure To Extract	• Broken or weak extractor spring	Replace
	• Silicon insert or reinforcement ring missing from extractor	Replace
	• Dirty, corroded ammunition	Remove and discard
	• Carbon in chamber	Clean chamber
	• Broken or worn extractor	Replace
	• Restricted buffer assembly	Remove and clean
	• Restricted movement of bolt and carrier assembly	Remove, clean, lubricate
	• Clogged gas tube	Replace
	• Short recoil	See "Short Recoil" below
Failure to Feed	• Dirty or corroded ammunition	Remove and discard
	• Dirty or damaged magazine	Clean or replace
	• Too many rounds in magazine	Remove excess rounds
	• Restricted buffer assembly	Remove and clean
	• Magazine not fully seated	Re-seat magazine, adjust magazine catch
	• Short recoil	See "Short Recoil" below
Double Feed	• Defective magazine	Replace
Failure to Chamber	• Dirty or corroded ammunition	Remove and discard
	• Carbon in carrier key or chamber	Clean
Does Not Fully Lock	• Dirt, corrosion, or carbon build-up in barrel locking lugs	Clean lugs
Short Recoil	• Carbon or dirt in carrier key or on outside of gas tube	Clean
	• Q-tip/pipe cleaner stuck inside carrier key	Remove
	• Weak or out-of-spec ammunition	Replace
Bolt Fails to Lock Open After Last Round	• Defective or damaged magazine	Replace
	• Dirty or corroded bolt catch	Clean or Replace
	• Weak or out-of-spec ammunition	Replace
Selector Lever Binds	• Needs oil	Lubricate
	• Dirt or sand under trigger	Clean
Bolt Carrier Jammed	• Round jammed between bolt and top of the receiver	See corrective action below

1) Place the firearm on SAFE.
2) Remove magazine.
3) Collapse the buttstock.
4) Push in on bottom of bolt catch.
5) While pulling down on charging handle, hit rifle butt on ground, bolt carrier should shift to rear; repeat as needed to clear the weapon.
6) While bolt is held to rear, round should fall out through magazine well.

NOTE: *If this procedure fails, use a cleaning rod to push the bolt fully to the rear.*

Using and Servicing the AR-15
Ammunition Warning

Use only domestic, commercially manufactured ammunition or high-quality surplus NATO-specification ammunition. Using any reloaded ammunition or any steel-cased ammunition may void your rifle's warranty. When purchasing domestically produced ammunition, questions can be answered by contacting the manufacturer directly. They will have the most accurate information about their products. If you have a problem with any ammunition, be sure to have the lot number from the packaging of the ammunition in question; the manufacturer will need this information. When purchasing surplus ammunition, it is not likely that the manufacturer is known or can be contacted. Most surplus ammunition is not from questionable sources, but some surplus ammunition is from rejected lots that did not meet a required specification. Find out as much as you can or purchase a small sample of the surplus ammunition before purchasing larger quantities. Many message boards will also have posts with reviews on ammunition by members. While these resources do not represent the final authority on ammunition-related issues, they serve as a helpful guide for general information concerning various types of ammunition. Inspect each cartridge for defects *before firing any ammunition*.

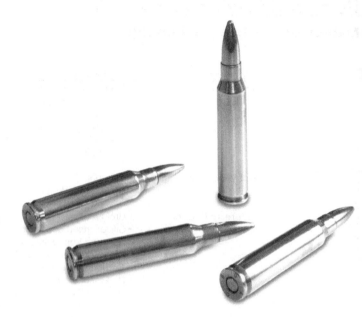

Dispose of cartridges that exhibit any of the following defects:

- **Deformed brass.** Including burrs, cracks, dents, scratches, bent or bowed cases.

- **Deformed bullet.** Including burrs, dents, and scratches.

- **Improperly seated bullets.** The case neck should be uniform, with no deformations, and the bullet should be seated tightly in the case. Check overall length to ensure the bullet is not seated too deeply or has been pushed in from an impact. Some ammunition may have a colored sealant around the case neck.

- **Improperly seated primers.** The primer should be flush with the base of the case, with no visible damage to the primer cup. Some ammunition may have a colored sealant around the primer.

- **Corroded cartridges.** Any amount of metal that is corroded and eaten away.

- Do not fire cartridges exposed to extreme heat (135 F°) until they have cooled.

Warning Signs
Not all defective ammunition has visible traits to distinguish it from good ammunition. If any cartridge from a lot of ammunition exhibits any of the following characteristics,

discontinue the use of the entire lot and contact the manufacturer or properly dispose of the ammunition.

1. Inconsistent function. This can also be a firearm-related malfunction. Clean and test the rifle with another source of ammunition. If proper function is restored, immediately discontinue the use of the suspect ammunition.

2. Blown primers. This is an indication of improper powder charge. Immediately discontinue the use of the suspect ammunition.

3. Inconsistent sound. Noticeably louder or quieter reports indicate improper powder charge. Immediately discontinue the use of the suspect ammunition.

4. Cartridge fails to chamber. This can also be a firearm-related malfunction. Clean and test the rifle with another source of ammunition. If proper function is restored, immediately discontinue the use of the suspect ammunition.

Other ammunition related problems can occur. If you believe that ammunition you are using is performing in an inconsistent manner, do not take any chances that you are experiencing a one-time occurrence. Discontinue the use of the suspect ammunition and contact the manufacturer.

Your rifle is a sizable investment. Make every effort to use quality ammunition to ensure your safety and prolong the life of your firearm for years of enjoyment.

Made in United States
Orlando, FL
28 October 2024

53215806R00050